101

Puzzles, Quizzes and Other Stuff

101 more things to do with children and young people

FREE CD OF PRINTABLE PUZZLES

DayOne

ISBN 978-1-84625-277-8

British Library Cataloguing in Publication Data available

Published by Day One Publications

Ryelands Road, Leominster, England, HR6 8NZ

Telephone 01568 613 740   FAX 01568 611 473

email—sales@dayone.co.uk

web site—www.dayone.co.uk

North American e-mail—usasales@dayone.co.uk

North American web site—www.dayonebookstore.com

Printed by Thomson Litho, East Kilbride, Scotland

Contents

 WE HOPE YOU FIND THIS BOOK USEFUL. WE HAVE ENCLOSED A FREE CD WITH PDFS OF ALL THE PUZZLES FOR EASE OF PRINTING.

Dedication
For Naomi, Joshua and Isaac Taylor

CODE BREAKERS

1 Codebreaker

Find the memory verse by breaking the code!

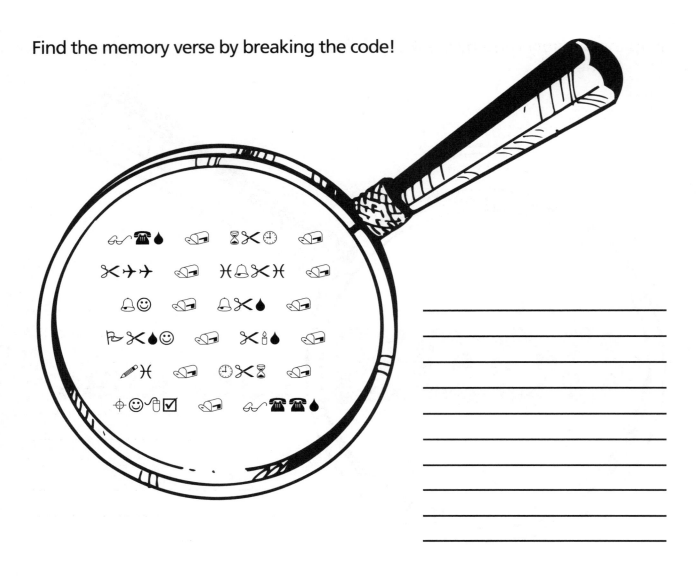

_____

_____

_____

_____

_____

_____

_____

_____

_____

_____

Use the information below to help you!

A	B	C	D	E	F	G	H	I	J	K	L	M	N	O	P

Q	R	S	T	U	V	W	X	Y	Z

This verse can be found in _____ chapter _____ verse _____.

2 Codebreaker

Find the memory verse by breaking the code!

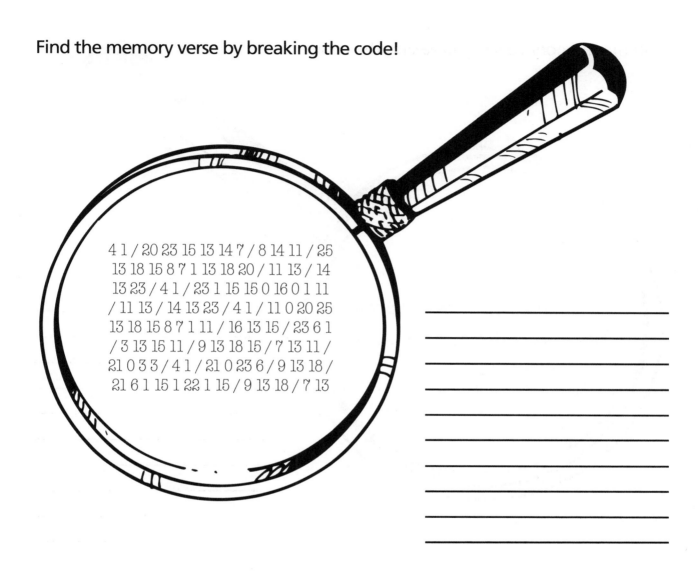

```
4 1 / 20 23 15 13 14 7 / 8 14 11 / 25
13 18 15 8 7 1 13 18 20 / 11 13 / 14
13 23 / 4 1 / 23 1 15 15 0 16 0 11
/ 11 13 / 14 13 23 / 4 1 / 11 0 20 25
13 18 15 8 7 1 11 / 16 13 15 / 23 6 1
/ 3 13 15 11 / 9 13 18 15 / 7 13 11 /
21 0 3 3 / 4 1 / 21 0 23 6 / 9 13 18 /
21 6 1 15 1 22 1 15 / 9 13 18 / 7 13
```

_____
_____
_____
_____
_____
_____
_____
_____
_____
_____

Use the information below to help you!

A	B	C	D	E	F	G	H	I	J	K	L	M	N	O	P
8	4	25	11	1	16	7	6	0	10	12	3	24	14	13	17

Q	R	S	T	U	V	W	X	Y	Z
5	15	20	23	18	22	21	9	2	19

This verse can be found in _____ chapter _____ verse _____.

3 Codebreaker

Find the memory verse by breaking the code!

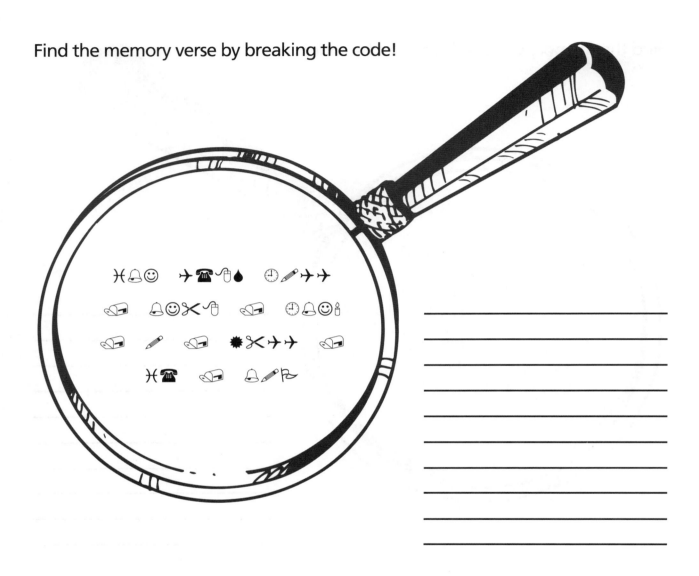

Use the information below to help you!

A	B	C	D	E	F	G	H	I	J	K	L	M	N	O	P
✂	©	®	♦	☺	♨	⌒	♘	✎	❄	☼	✈	⚑	♪	☎	💻

Q	R	S	T	U	V	W	X	Y	Z
♈	⌒	⧖	♓	★	⊕	⊕	⊠	☑	✼

This verse can be found in _____ chapter _____ verse _____.

4 Codebreaker

Find the memory verse by breaking the code!

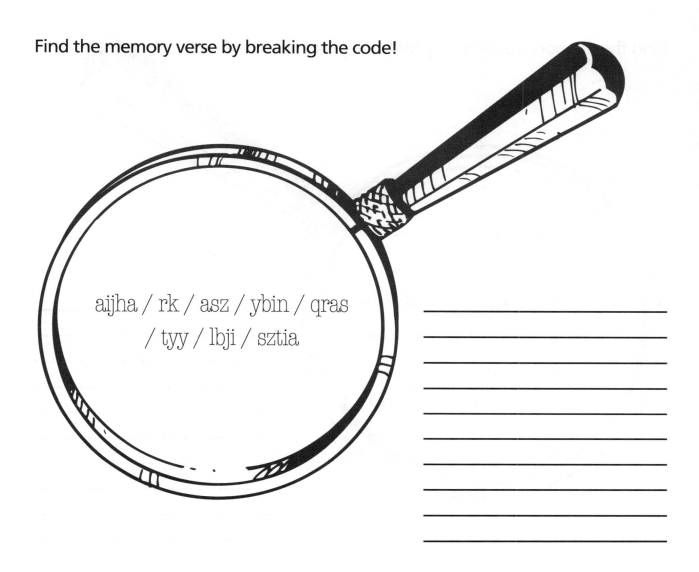

aijha / rk / asz / ybin / qras / tyy / lbji / sztia

_____
_____
_____
_____
_____
_____
_____
_____
_____

Use the information below to help you!

A	B	C	D	E	F	G	H	I	J	K	L	M	N	O	P
t	p	d	n	z	m	o	s	r	u	c	y	f	k	b	g

Q	R	S	T	U	V	W	X	Y	Z
w	i	h	a	j	x	q	v	l	e

This verse can be found in _____ chapter _____ verse _____.

5 Codebreaker

Find the memory verse by breaking the code!

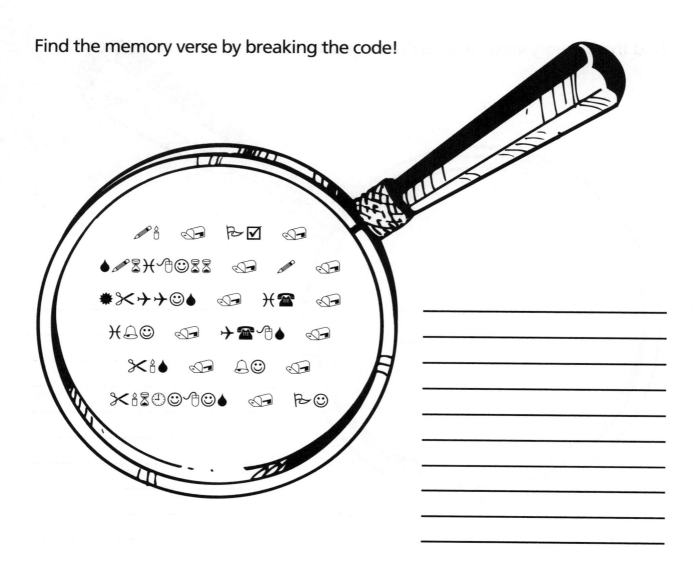

Use the information below to help you!

A	B	C	D	E	F	G	H	I	J	K	L	M	N	O	P

Q	R	S	T	U	V	W	X	Y	Z

This verse can be found in _____ chapter _____ verse _____.

6 Codebreaker

Find the memory verse by breaking the code!

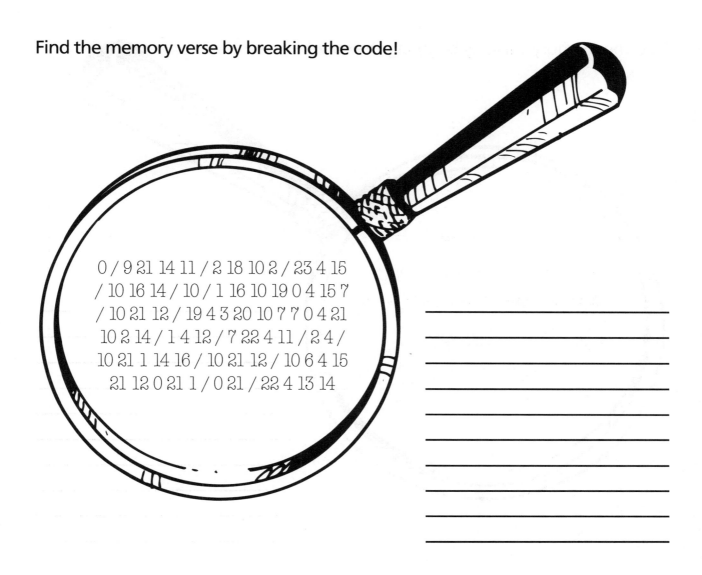

0 / 9 21 14 11 / 2 18 10 2 / 23 4 15
/ 10 16 14 / 10 / 1 16 10 19 0 4 15 7
/ 10 21 12 / 19 4 3 20 10 7 7 0 4 21
10 2 14 / 1 4 12 / 7 22 4 11 / 2 4 /
10 21 1 14 16 / 10 21 12 / 10 6 4 15
21 12 0 21 1 / 0 21 / 22 4 13 14

_____
_____
_____
_____
_____
_____
_____
_____
_____

Use the information below to help you!

A	B	C	D	E	F	G	H	I	J	K	L	M	N	O	P
10	6	19	12	14	25	1	18	0	8	9	22	3	21	4	20

	Q	R	S	T	U	V	W	X	Y	Z
	17	16	7	2	15	13	11	24	23	5

This verse can be found in _____ chapter _____ verse _____ .

7 Codebreaker

Find the memory verse by breaking the code!

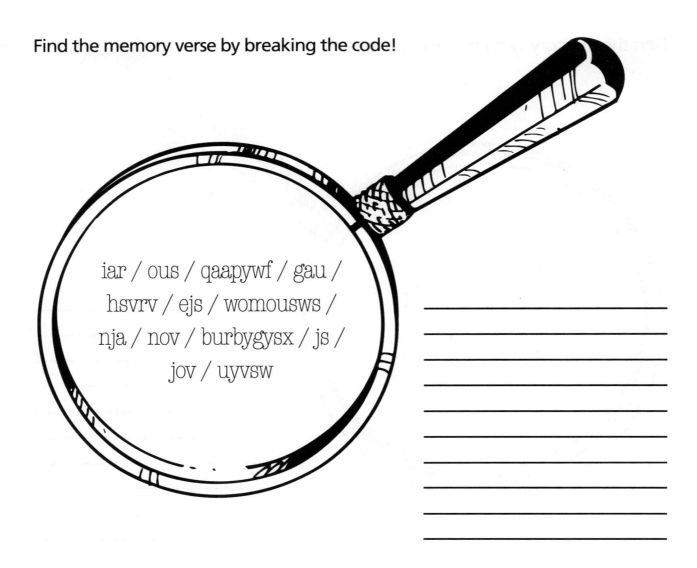

iar / ous / qaapywf / gau / hsvrv / ejs / womousws / nja / nov / burbygysx / js / jov / uyvsw

_____
_____
_____
_____
_____
_____
_____
_____
_____
_____

Use the information below to help you!

A	B	C	D	E	F	G	H	I	J	K	L	M	N	O	P
o	c	b	x	s	g	f	j	y	h	p	q	z	w	a	k

Q	R	S	T	U	V	W	X	Y	Z
l	u	v	e	r	t	n	d	i	m

This verse can be found in _____ chapter _____ verse _____.

8 Codebreaker

Find the memory verse by breaking the code!

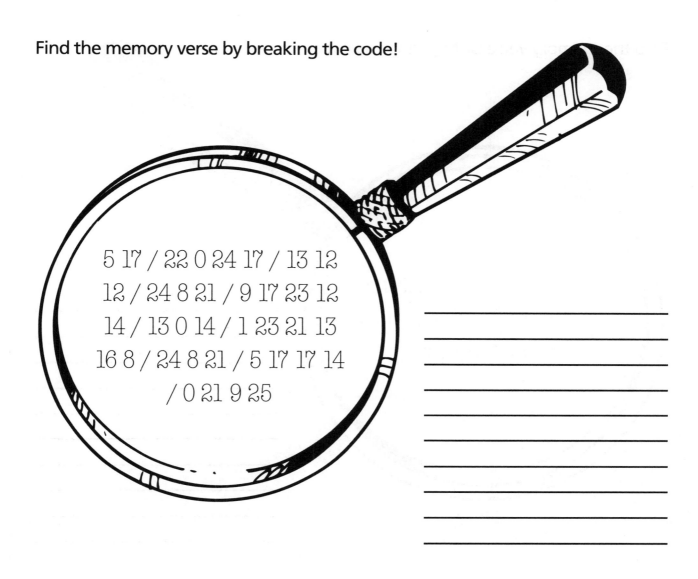

5 17 / 22 0 24 17 / 13 12
12 / 24 8 21 / 9 17 23 12
14 / 13 0 14 / 1 23 21 13
16 8 / 24 8 21 / 5 17 17 14
/ 0 21 9 25

_____
_____
_____
_____
_____
_____
_____
_____
_____

Use the information below to help you!

A	B	C	D	E	F	G	H	I	J	K	L	M	N	O	P
13	15	16	14	21	6	5	8	22	7	20	12	11	0	17	1

Q	R	S	T	U	V	W	X	Y	Z
2	23	25	24	10	4	9	3	19	18

This verse can be found in _____ chapter _____ verse _____.

9 Codebreaker

Find the memory verse by breaking the code!

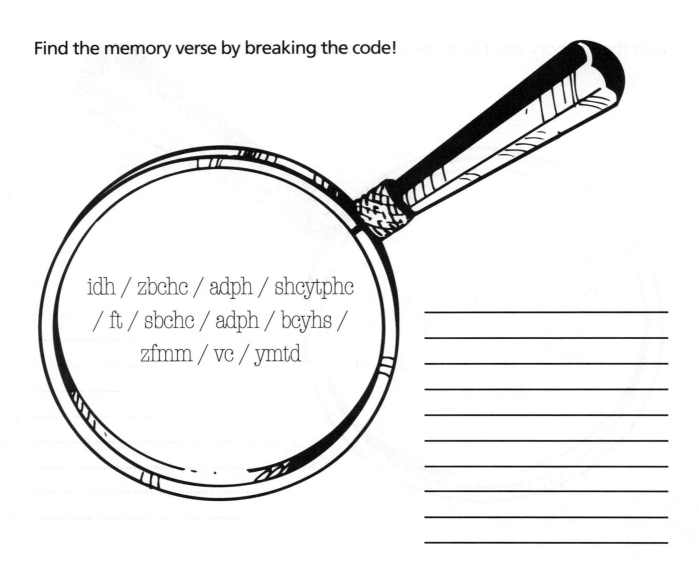

idh / zbchc / adph / shcytphc / ft / sbchc / adph / bcyhs / zfmm / vc / ymtd

_____
_____
_____
_____
_____
_____
_____
_____
_____
_____

Use the information below to help you!

A	B	C	D	E	F	G	H	I	J	K	L	M	N	O	P
y	v	e	o	c	i	k	b	f	n	g	m	l	j	d	u

Q	R	S	T	U	V	W	X	Y	Z
x	h	t	s	p	r	z	q	a	w

This verse can be found in _____ chapter _____ verse _____.

10 Codebreaker

Find the memory verse by breaking the code!

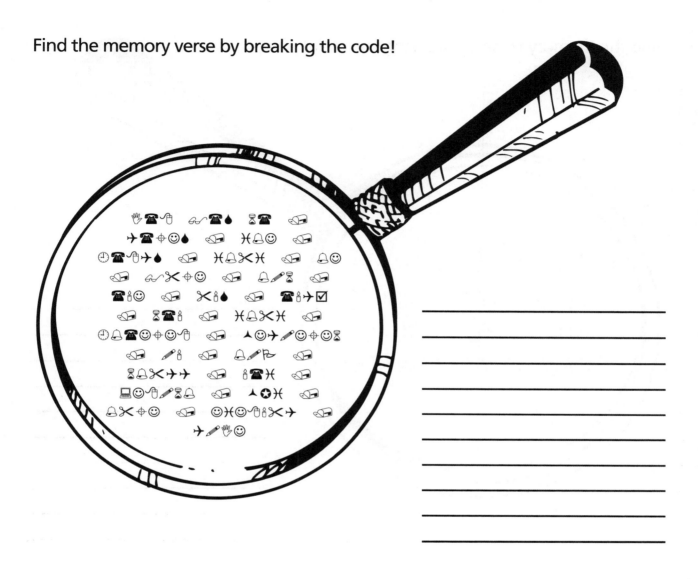

_____

_____

_____

_____

_____

_____

_____

_____

_____

Use the information below to help you!

A	B	C	D	E	F	G	H	I	J	K	L	M	N	O	P

Q	R	S	T	U	V	W	X	Y	Z

This verse can be found in _____ chapter _____ verse _____.

11 Codebreaker

Find the memory verse by breaking the code!

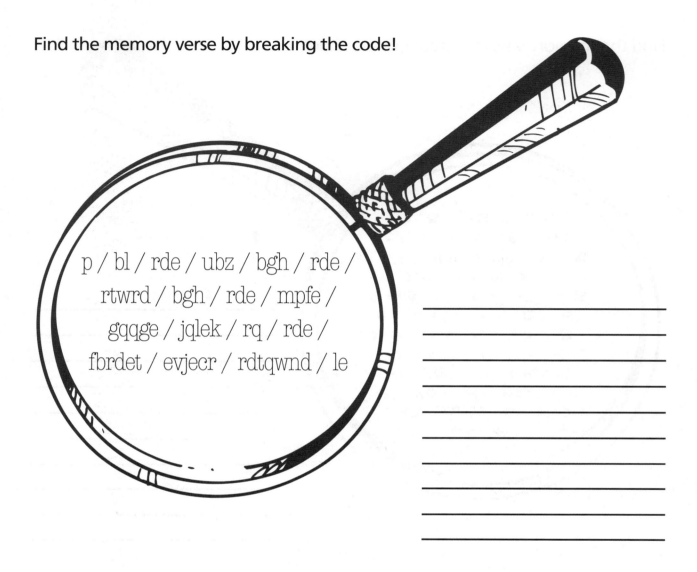

p / bl / rde / ubz / bgh / rde /
rtwrd / bgh / rde / mpfe /
gqqge / jqlek / rq / rde /
fbrdet / evjecr / rdtqwnd / le

_____

_____

_____

_____

_____

_____

_____

_____

_____

Use the information below to help you!

A	B	C	D	E	F	G	H	I	J	K	L	M	N	O	P
b	a	j	h	e	f	n	d	p	i	s	m	l	g	q	c

Q	R	S	T	U	V	W	X	Y	Z
o	t	k	r	w	x	u	v	z	y

This verse can be found in _____ chapter _____ verse _____.

12 Codebreaker

Find the memory verse by breaking the code!

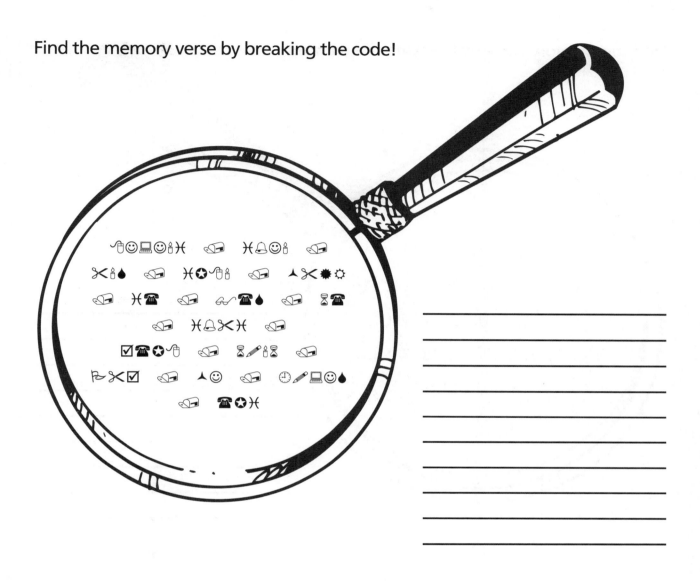

_____

_____

_____

_____

_____

_____

_____

_____

_____

Use the information below to help you!

A	B	C	D	E	F	G	H	I	J	K	L	M	N	O	P

Q	R	S	T	U	V	W	X	Y	Z

This verse can be found in _____ chapter _____ verse _____.

Find the memory verse by breaking the code!

rdjedpmut / mr / zuvtb / mt / tuuto / ojro / zus / pnoso / mr / tu / upnos / tdio / vtbos / nodeot / xmeot / pu / iot / cw / ynman / yo / ivrp / co / rdeob

_____
_____
_____
_____
_____
_____
_____
_____
_____
_____

Use the information below to help you!

A	B	C	D	E	F	G	H	I	J	K	L	M	N	O	P
d	c	a	b	o	z	x	n	m	l	q	j	i	t	u	h

Q	R	S	T	U	V	W	X	Y	Z
k	s	r	p	v	e	y	g	w	f

This verse can be found in _____ chapter _____ verse _____.

Codebreaker

Find the memory verse by breaking the code!

18 17 / 12 7 25 / 15 7 11 17 3 8 8 / 0
18 21 16 / 12 7 25 5 / 24 7 25 21 16 /
13 3 8 25 8 / 18 8 / 10 7 5 4 / 22 11 4 /
23 3 10 18 3 19 3 / 18 11 / 12 7 25 5
/ 16 3 22 5 21 / 14 4 / 5 22 18 8 3 4 /
16 18 24 / 17 5 7 24 / 21 16 3 / 4 3 22
4 / 12 7 25 / 0 18 10 10 / 23 3 / 8 22
19 3 4

_____
_____
_____
_____
_____
_____
_____
_____
_____
_____

Use the information below to help you!

A	B	C	D	E	F	G	H	I	J	K	L	M	N	O	P
22	23	15	4	3	17	14	16	18	13	9	10	24	11	7	2

			Q	R	S	T	U	V	W	X	Y	Z
			6	5	8	21	25	19	0	1	12	20

This verse can be found in _____ chapter _____ verse _____.

15 Codebreaker

Find the memory verse by breaking the code!

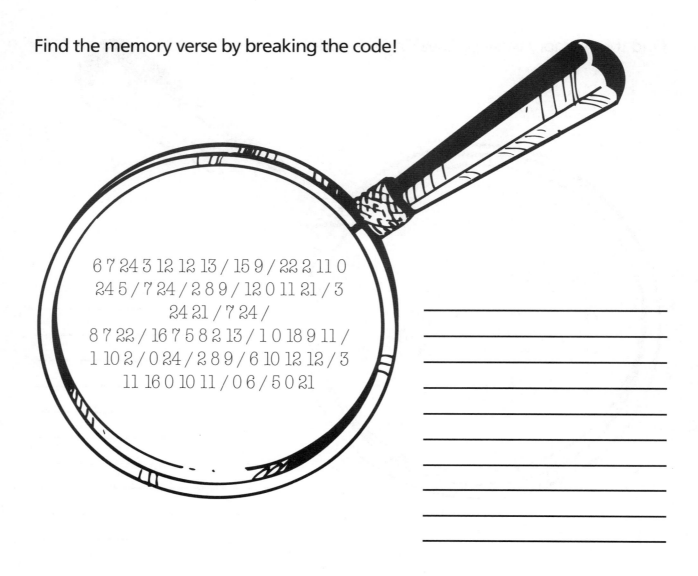

6 7 24 3 12 12 13 / 15 9 / 22 2 11 0
24 5 / 7 24 / 2 8 9 / 12 0 11 21 / 3
24 21 / 7 24 /
8 7 22 / 16 7 5 8 2 13 / 10 18 9 11 /
1 10 2 / 0 24 / 2 8 9 / 6 10 12 12 / 3
11 16 0 10 11 / 0 6 / 5 0 21

_____
_____
_____
_____
_____
_____
_____
_____
_____

Use the information below to help you!

A	B	C	D	E	F	G	H	I	J	K	L	M	N	O	P
3	15	19	21	9	6	5	8	7	4	17	12	16	24	0	1

Q	R	S	T	U	V	W	X	Y	Z
20	11	22	2	10	14	18	25	13	23

This verse can be found in _____ chapter _____ verse _____.

16 Codebreaker

Find the memory verse by breaking the code!

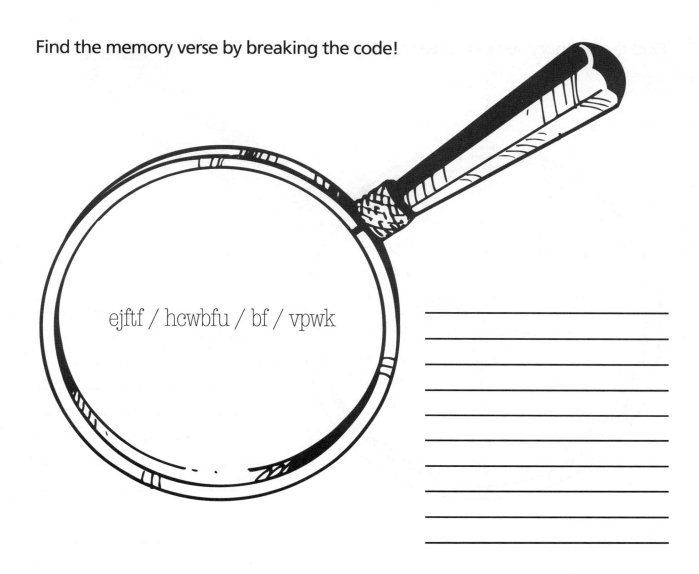

ejftf / hcwbfu / bf / vpwk

_____

_____

_____

_____

_____

_____

_____

_____

_____

_____

Use the information below to help you!

A	B	C	D	E	F	G	H	I	J	K	L	M	N	O	P
r	i	h	k	j	s	m	c	b	e	d	v	g	y	p	o

Q	R	S	T	U	V	W	X	Y	Z
a	w	f	u	t	l	q	z	n	x

This verse can be found in _____ chapter _____ verse _____.

17 Codebreaker

Find the memory verse by breaking the code!

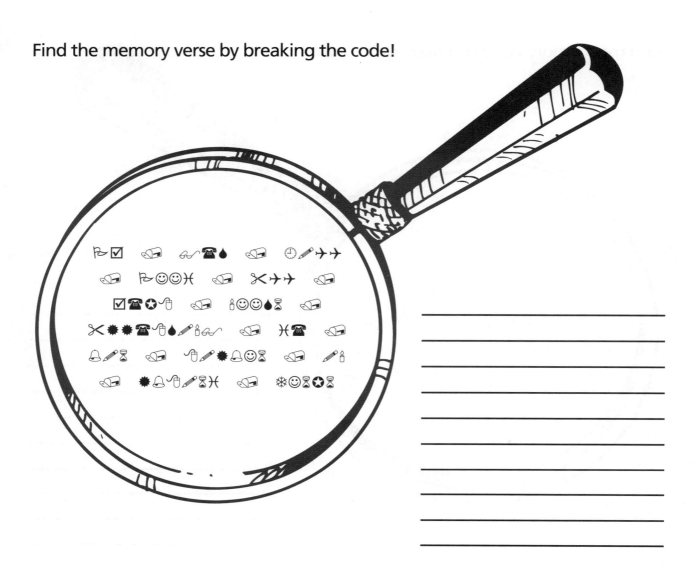

Use the information below to help you!

A	B	C	D	E	F	G	H	I	J	K	L	M	N	O	P

Q	R	S	T	U	V	W	X	Y	Z

This verse can be found in _____ chapter _____ verse _____.

18 Codebreaker

Find the memory verse by breaking the code!

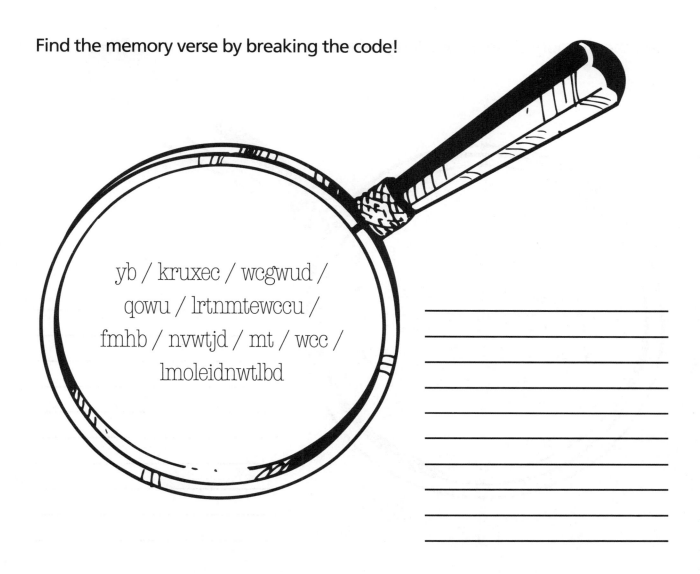

yb / kruxec / wcgwud / qowu / lrtnmtewccu / fmhb / nvwtjd / mt / wcc / lmoleidnwtlbd

_____
_____
_____
_____
_____
_____
_____
_____

Use the information below to help you!

A	B	C	D	E	F	G	H	I	J	K	L	M	N	O	P
w	y	l	s	b	x	f	v	m	k	j	c	i	t	r	q

Q	R	S	T	U	V	W	X	Y	Z
p	o	d	n	e	h	g	z	u	a

This verse can be found in _____ chapter _____ verse _____.

19 Codebreaker

Find the memory verse by breaking the code!

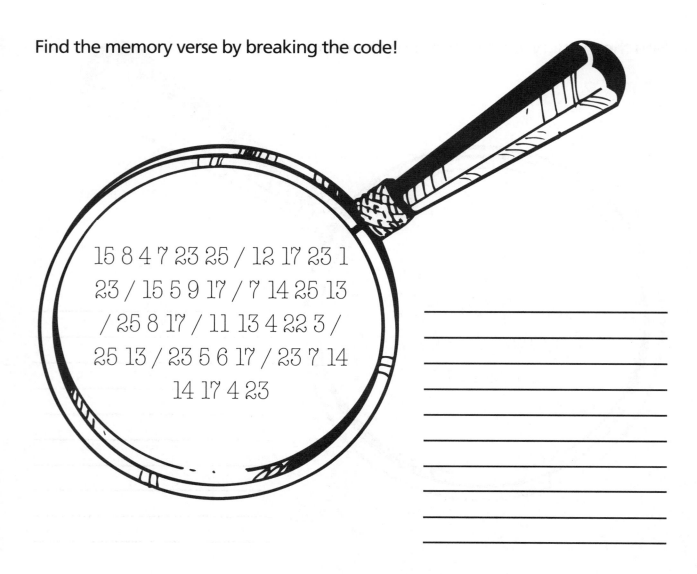

15 8 4 7 23 25 / 12 17 23 1 23 / 15 5 9 17 / 7 14 25 13 / 25 8 17 / 11 13 4 22 3 / 25 13 / 23 5 6 17 / 23 7 14 14 17 4 23

_____
_____
_____
_____
_____
_____
_____
_____
_____
_____

Use the information below to help you!

A	B	C	D	E	F	G	H	I	J	K	L	M	N	O	P
5	20	15	3	17	21	0	8	7	12	24	22	9	14	13	2

Q	R	S	T	U	V	W	X	Y	Z
16	4	23	25	1	6	11	18	10	19

This verse can be found in _____ chapter _____ verse _____.

Codebreaker

Find the memory verse by breaking the code!

8 16 5 / 12 10 5 / 11 16 12 / 23 15
/ 23 10 / 14 12 24 / 23 15 / 2 9 5 3
8 5 9 / 8 16 3 10 / 8 16 5 / 12 10 5
/ 11 16 12 / 23 15 / 23 10 / 8 16 5 /
11 12 9 22 0

_____
_____
_____
_____
_____
_____
_____
_____
_____
_____
_____

Use the information below to help you!

A	B	C	D	E	F	G	H	I	J	K	L	M	N	O	P
3	21	6	0	5	4	2	16	23	7	13	22	20	10	12	18

Q	R	S	T	U	V	W	X	Y	Z
17	9	15	8	24	1	11	25	14	19

This verse can be found in _____ chapter _____ verse _____.

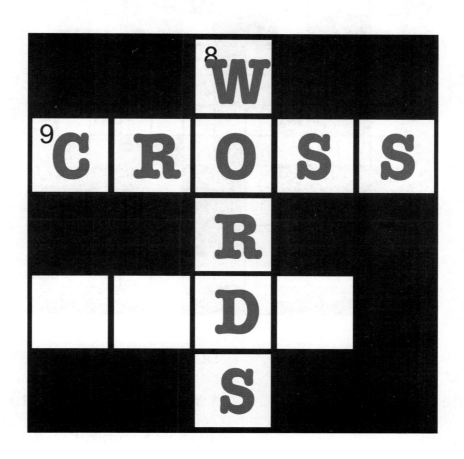

21 The Ten Commandments (Exod. 20:1-17)

ACROSS

2 Remember the ... day (7)

5 Do not ... (6)

8 The land the people were rescued from was one of ... (7)

9 The name of the country the people were rescued from (5)

12 There are ten of these (12)

DOWN

1 You shall have no other ... (4)

3 Do not commit ... (8)

4 ... your father and mother (6)

5 Do not ... the name of God (6)

6 Do not ... (5)

7 Do not give false ... (9)

10 Do not ... your neighbour's property (5)

11 Do not make an ... (4)

22 The golden calf Exod. 32

ACROSS

3 The people wanted ... to go before them (4)

5 The people went to ... to help them (5)

6 The sons of ... answered Moses' call to follow the Lord. (4)

8 God ... when Moses pleaded with him the first time (8)

10 ... was angry when he saw what the people did (5)

11 God sent a ... to punish them (6)

DOWN

1 The tablets containing the Ten ... were broken into pieces at the foot of the mountain (12)

2 Moses was Aaron's ... (7)

3 The idol was made out of ... (4)

4 God described the people as ... (11)

7 The shape of the idol (4)

9 Joshua said there was a noise of ... in the camp (3)

23 The twelve tribes of Israel

ACROSS

2 G ... (3)

4 B ... (8)

7 I ... (8)

10 M ... (8)

11 L ... (4)

12 R ... (6)

DOWN

1 J ... (5)

3 D ... (3)

5 E ... (7)

6 N ... (8)

8 S ... (6)

9 Z ... (7)

24 The call of Gideon (Judg. 6:11-40)

ACROSS

1 Gideon tore down the altar during the ... (v. 27) (5)

4 An ... of the Lord spoke to Gideon (5)

6 Gideon was threshing wheat in a ... (9)

8 The altar was called 'The Lord is ...' (5)

10 The angel described Gideon as a man of ... (6)

DOWN

2 The son of Joash (6)

3 The altar Gideon tore down was an altar to ... (4)

5 The Midianites and Amalekites camped in the Valley of ... (7)

7 The age of the second bull (5)

9 This consumed the meat and the bread (backwards) (4)

25 Psalm 23

ACROSS

4 He leads me beside still … (6)

6 He restores my … (4)

7 The … is my shepherd (4)

8 He leads me in … of righteousness (5)

9 One thing that comforts me (5)

DOWN

1 I shall not be in … (4)

2 I lie in green … (8)

3 One thing that will follow me (8)

4 How do I get through the valley? (4)

5 I shall not fear … (4)

26 Jonah

ACROSS

1 After the men threw Jonah overboard the sea became … (4)

5 Jonah was … the fish for three days and nights (6)

6 The people of Nineveh believed in … (3)

DOWN

2 The fish spat Jonah onto dry … (4)

3 The men threw Jonah … (9)

4 Jonah was inside a big … (4)

27 People in the Old Testament

ACROSS

2 He brought Israel out of Egypt (5)

7 He built an ark (4)

8 She was the sister of Moses (6)

9 He was thrown into a lions' den (6)

10 He was the first man (4)

DOWN

1 She met her husband while working in a field (4)

3 He was very wise (7)

4 She had a baby called Samuel (6)

5 He was a shepherd boy (5)

6 His niece was called Esther (8)

28 Christmas (Matt. 1-2; Luke 2)

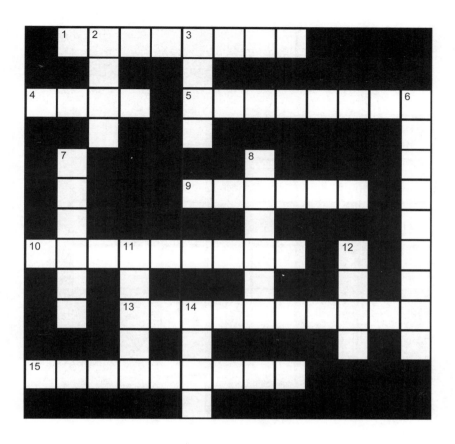

ACROSS

1 The shepherds were glorifying and … God (8)

4 The angel brought … news (4)

5 Caesar … issued a decree (8)

9 They laid the baby in a … (6)

10 Jesus was born in … (9)

13 Everyone went to his or her own town to be … (10)

15 Jesus was wrapped in … cloths (9)

DOWN

2 There was no … at the inn (4)

3 The wise men followed a … (4)

6 The angels appeared to … (9)

7 He was going to marry Mary (6)

8 The … brought the message to the shepherds (6)

11 … wanted Jesus killed (5)

12 The mother of Jesus (4)

14 One of the gifts from the wise men was … (4)

29 The baptism of Jesus (Matt. 3:13-17)

ACROSS

1 The name of the man who baptized Jesus (4)

5 The bird that the Holy Spirit appeared as (4)

6 You use this to speak (5)

7 Jesus is God's ... (3)

DOWN

1 The river Jesus was baptized in (6)

2 The voice came from here (6)

3 Jesus travelled from here to be baptized (7)

4 God said that this was his Son whom he ... (5)

30 The little children and Jesus (Mark 10:13-16)

ACROSS

2 When Jesus saw what was happening he was … (9)

6 Jesus … the children (7)

9 Opposite of big (6)

10 God's Son (5)

11 Not old (5)

DOWN

1 Jesus … the disciples (7)

3 They sent the children away (9)

4 The kingdom of … (3)

5 The people wanted Jesus to … the children (5)

7 They were brought to Jesus (8)

8 Jesus took the children in his … (4)

31 The feeding of the five thousand (Matt. 14:13-21)

ACROSS

1 The colour of grass (5)

3 Jesus's twelve friends were called … (9)

6 What you say when someone gives you something (6)

7 Jesus looked up to … (6)

8 The leftover food was collected in … (7)

11 2+3 = … (4)

DOWN

1 You cut this with a lawnmower (5)

2 The opposite of none (6)

4 They swim in the sea (4)

5 Jesus broke the … of bread (6)

6 The number of basketfuls left over (6)

9 The people … the food (3)

10 The number of fish Jesus started with (3)

32 Jesus calms the storm (Luke 8:22-25)

ACROSS

3 A small ship (4)

5 You can surf on these (5)

6 After Jesus spoke the sea was … (4)

8 You go to bed to do this … (5)

9 The disciples were … by what Jesus did (9)

DOWN

1 The disciples thought they were going to … (5)

2 Jesus calmed the … (5)

4 The disciples called Jesus this (7)

6 Jesus slept on this (7)

7 Jesus told the wind and waves to be … (5)

33 Jesus betrayed (Mark 14:43-52)

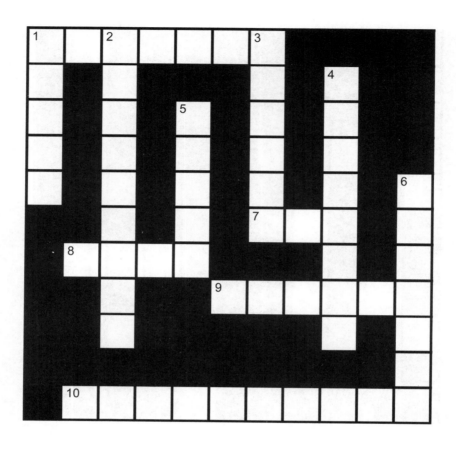

ACROSS

1 This man lost his ear (7)

7 You hear with this (3)

8 Jesus was greeted with a ... (4)

9 The servant of the high ... was there (6)

10 Jesus was betrayed in the garden of ... (10)

DOWN

1 Used to cut off the man's ear (5)

2 Jesus wasn't leading a ... (9)

3 The number of disciples (6)

4 Everyone ... Jesus (8)

5 He betrayed Jesus (5)

6 To take captive (7)

34 Peter denies Jesus (Matt. 26:69-75; Luke 22:54-62)

ACROSS

1 Peter sat by one of these (4)

3 Sixty minutes makes one (4)

5 Jesus ... at Peter (6)

7 The noise a rooster makes (5)

8 Peter went outside and ... (4)

9 The disciple called the Rock (5)

10 How many times Peter denied Jesus (5)

11 The people called Peter a ... (8)

DOWN

1 To go after someone (6)

2 Jesus was taken to the high priest's ... (5)

4 A male chicken (7)

6 Peter ... that he knew Jesus (6)

7 The fire was in the middle of a ... (9)

35 Jesus's death and resurrection

ACROSS

1 This man gave his tomb to Jesus (Matt. 27:57–60) (6)

3 The mother of Jesus (4)

7 They cast ... for his clothing (Matt. 27:35) (4)

9 The soldiers made Jesus wear a scarlet ... (Matt. 27:28) (4)

10 They laid Jesus here after he died (Matt. 27:60) (4)

12 Jesus was ... of any crime (Matt. 27:4) (8)

14 The twelve friends of Jesus were called ... (9)

15 The place where Jesus died (Matt. 27:33) (8)

DOWN

2 Jesus died so that people could be forgiven for their ... (4)

4 The angel said, 'He is not here; he is ...' (Matt. 28:6) (5)

5 While Jesus died the land was in ... (Matt. 27:45) (8)

6 Two thieves were ... with Jesus (Matt. 27:38) (9)

8 The soldiers made Jesus a crown of ... (Matt. 27:29) (6)

11 Jesus shed his ... for our sins (5)

13 Jesus was betrayed for ... pieces of silver (Matt. 27:3) (6)

36 The Gospels

ACROSS

3 What was Luke's job? (6)

5 The second Gospel (4)

6 Who are the Gospels about? (5)

7 The Gospels are in the …
Testament (3)

8 The third Gospel (4)

DOWN

1 Gospel means … News (4)

2 How many Gospels are there? (4)

4 The first four books in the New
Testament are the … (7)

5 The first Gospel (7)

6 The fourth Gospel (4)

37 The armour of God (Eph. 6:10-18)

ACROSS

1 The Lord has mighty ... (5)

4 What must you do on all occasions? (4)

6 Who must you stand against? (5)

9 Put on the ... of righteousness (11)

11 Buckle on the belt of ... (5)

12 Be ... in the Lord (6)

13 The sword of the ... (6)

DOWN

2 The shoes of ... (9)

3 The shield of ... (5)

5 Who is your struggle against? (11)

7 The gospel of ... (5)

8 The helmet of ... (9)

10 Put on the full ... of God (6)

38 The letter to Philemon

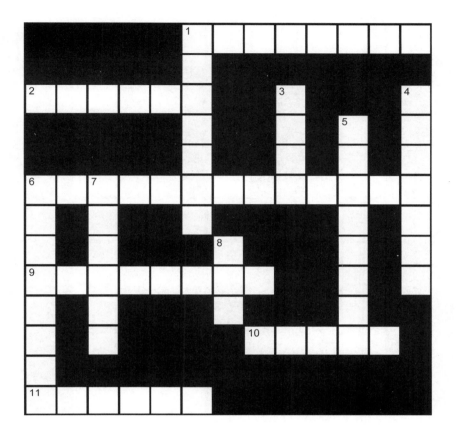

ACROSS

1 Paul was a … of Christ Jesus (8)

2 Who was 'our sister'? (6)

6 One thing Philemon's love gave Paul (13)

9 Who was the fellow-worker? (8)

10 What sort of room did Paul want? (5)

11 Who had Philemon refreshed the hearts of? (6)

DOWN

1 Paul thanked God in his … (7)

3 Where did the church meet? (4)

4 What did Paul ask Philemon to consider Onesimus as? (7)

5 Who did Paul send back to Philemon? (8)

6 Who was Paul's fellow-prisoner? (8)

7 Paul wanted his heart refreshing in … (6)

8 A second thing Philemon's love gave Paul (3)

39 The letters to the seven churches (Rev. 2-3)

ACROSS

1 The church which persevered (7)

5 The lukewarm church (8)

6 The church that suffered (6)

DOWN

2 The faithful church (8)

3 The dead church (6)

4 The church that was misled (8)

40 Mothers in the Bible

ACROSS

3 The mother of Isaac (Gen. 21:3) (5)

5 The mother of Abijah (2 Chr. 13:2) (6)

6 The mother of Jotham (2 Chr. 27:1) (8)

7 The mother of Amon (2 Kings 21:19) (12)

10 The mother of Jacob (Gen. 25:28) (7)

11 The mother of Mahlon (Ruth 1:2) (5)

13 The mother of Cain (Gen. 4:1) (3)

14 The mother of Obed (Ruth 4:13–17) (4)

DOWN

1 The mother of Solomon (2 Sam. 12:24) (9)

2 The mother of Joseph (Gen. 35:24) (6)

4 The mother of Samuel (1 Sam. 1:20) (6)

8 The mother of Reuben (Gen. 35:23) (4)

9 The mother of John (Luke 1:57) (9)

12 The mother of Jesus (Luke 1:30–31) (4)

QUESTIONS AND ANSWERS

41 Creation (Gen. 1-2)

Write the answer to each question.

1. What did God create on day one?

2. What did God create on day two?

3. What did God create on day three?

4. What did God create on day four?

5. What did God create on day five?

6. What did God create on day six?

7. What did God do on day seven?

8. What was the name of the first man?

9. What was missing when Adam looked at the animals?

10. What was the name of the first woman?

11. From what did God make Eve?

12. What did God create for Adam and Eve to live in?

13. What was the name of the garden?

14. From what did God create Adam?

15. How did God bring Adam to life?

42 The Fall (Gen. 3)

Write the answer to each question.

1. What did God tell Adam and Eve to do?

2. God placed two special trees in the Garden of Eden. Name one.

3. Name the second.

4. What did God say about the tree of the knowledge of good and evil?

5. Which creature came and spoke to Eve?

6. Who was the serpent really?

7. What did the serpent say to her?

8. What did Eve do after the serpent had spoken to her

9. What did Adam and Eve do when they heard God coming?

10. What did they make to hide themselves?

11. What excuse did Adam make for eating the fruit?

12. What did God make for them to hide their shame?

13. What was God's response to what they had done?

14. What happened to Adam and Eve?

15. What did God do to make things right again?

43 Cain and Abel (Gen. 4:1-17)

Write the answer to each question.

1. What were the names of Adam and Eve's first sons?

2. What was Cain's job?

3. What was Abel's job?

4. What did Abel sacrifice to God?

5. What did Cain sacrifice to God?

6. Whose sacrifice was God pleased with?

7. How did Cain feel about this?

8. What did Cain ask Abel to do?

9. What did Cain do when they got to the field?

10. What did God say to Cain?

11. What was Cain's answer?

12. What did God put on Cain to protect him?

13. Where did Cain move to?

14. What was Cain's son called?

15. When Cain built a city, who did he name it after?

44 Noah (Gen. 6–9)

Write the answer to each question.

1. Why did God determine to destroy the people on earth?

2. Who was the one person who found favour with God?

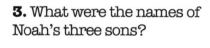

3. What were the names of Noah's three sons?

4. How long did God send the rain for?

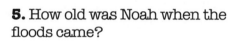

5. How old was Noah when the floods came?

6. How many people were saved when the floods came?

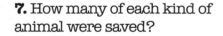

7. How many of each kind of animal were saved?

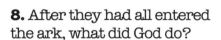

8. After they had all entered the ark, what did God do?

9. For how many days did the water cover the earth?

10. On which mountain did the ark land?

11. What was the first creature Noah sent out from the ark?

12. What was the second creature that was sent out from the ark?

13. When she came back the second time, the dove had something in her mouth. What was it?

14. After Noah and his family left the ark, what did he do?

15. What sign did God send as a promise thst he wouldn't flood the earth again?

45 Abraham and Lot (Gen. 13-14)

Write the answer to each question.

1. Where did Abraham and Lot live?

2. Were they rich or poor?

3. What was the relationship between Abraham and Lot?

4. When Lot and Abraham's herdsmen started to argue, what did Abram suggest?

5. Who chose the direction he wanted to go in first?

6. Where did Lot go?

7. Where did Abraham go?

8. What sort of city was Sodom?

9. Did Lot really choose the best way?

10. Who was Lot captured by?

11. What did Abraham do when he heard what had happened?

12. How many men did Abraham take with him to rescue Lot?

13. Where did Lot go after he was rescued?

14. After Abraham's victory, which king of Salem came out to meet him?

15. What proportion of his possessions did Abraham give to Melchizedek?

46 Joseph—the early years (Gen. 37)

Write the answer to each question.

1. Who was Joseph's father?

2. Who was Joseph's mother?

3. What happened to his mother?

4. How many brothers and sisters did Joseph have?

5. Who was Jacob's favourite child?

6. What special thing did Jacob give to Joseph?

7. What did Joseph's brothers think about him?

8. What was Joseph's first dream?

9. How did Joseph's brothers interpret the dream?

10. What was Joseph's second dream?

11. What was the meaning of this dream?

12. What did Joseph's brothers plan to do to him?

13. Who intervened to save Joseph?

14. What did they do with Joseph?

15. Who bought Joseph?

47 Job

Write the answer to each question.

1. Where did Job live?

2. How did God describe Job?

3. On the day the sons of God came before God, who else came?

4. God said that Satan could touch Job's possessions, but what couldn't he touch?

5. Job lost his children and animals in how many days?

6. God then said that Satan could touch Job, but what couldn't he do?

7. What was Job's body covered in?

8. Who told Job that he should 'curse God and die'?

9. What were Job's three friends called?

10. When Job's friends first came, for how long did no one speak?

11. Why didn't they talk?

12. Towards the end of the book, how did God answer Job?

13. Who was to pray for Job's three friends?

14. After Job prayed for his friends, what did God do for him?

15. When all his friends and relatives came to celebrate with him, what did they bring?

48 Jonah

Write the answer to each question.

1. Where was Jonah sent by God to preach?

2. Where did Jonah's ship sail from?

3. Where was Jonah trying to flee to?

4. What happened while he was on the boat?

5. What did the sailors do when they became afraid during the storm?

6. What did Jonah tell them to do?

7. How long was Jonah in the fish?

8. What did Jonah do inside the fish?

9. What happened on the third day?

10. What did God say to Jonah?

11. When Jonah finally got to Ninevah, what did he preach?

12. What did the Ninevites do?

13. How did Jonah react when he saw that God had compassion on the people?

14. What did God provide for Jonah's shelter?

15. What happened to the vine?

49 The prophets

Write the answer to each question.

1. Which king died in the year in which Isaiah had a vision of God on his throne?

2. How long did Jeremiah predict the captivity would last for?

3. What was Ezekiel's job?

4. Which king took Daniel to Babylon?

5. Who was Hosea's wife?

6. Which insects are mentioned in lots of Joel's prophecies?

7. Amos mentioned a specific type of famine the people would suffer. What was it?

8. Obadiah preached judgement against which country?

9. Micah predicted that Christ would be born where?

10. Nahum prophesised against which city?

11. To which nation did God tell Habakkuk he was going to send the Jews to punish them?

12. Zephaniah urged the people to do what?

13. Haggai told the people to rebuild what?

14. How many chariots did Zechariah see in his vision?

15. Malachi told the people they had robbed God by not doing what?

50 Jesus's childhood (Luke 2:41–52)

Write the answer to each question.

1. Who were Jesus's earthly parents?

2. Who was Jesus's real father?

3. What job did Joseph do?

4. Where did Jesus grow up?

5. To where did his parents take him for safety as a baby?

6. How old was Jesus when his parents took him to the temple in Jerusalem?

7. Why did they go to the temple?

8. How long was Jesus missing before his parents noticed?

9. How long was it before they found him?

10. Where did they find Jesus?

11. What was he doing?

12. How did the people react to his questions?

13. When Mary asked Jesus why he had stayed, what did he say?

14. What happened when Jesus went home?

15. How did Mary react?

51 Jesus's baptism and temptation
(Matt. 3:13-4:11; Mark 1:9-13; Luke 3:21-23; 4:1-13)

Write the answer to each question.

1. Who was baptizing people in the desert?

2. What did John say to Jesus when Jesus asked him to baptize him?

3. What creature settled on Jesus after he had been baptized?

4. Who appeared like a dove?

5. What did the voice from heaven say?

6. What did John the Baptist wear?

7. What did John the Baptist eat?

8. Where was Jesus baptized?

9. How did John know Jesus?

10. Why was Jesus baptized?

11. Where did the Holy Spirit send Jesus after he was baptized?

12. How long was Jesus in the desert for?

13. What happened to Jesus while he was in the desert?

14. Each time Jesus was tempted, he answered using what?

15. Who ministered to Jesus in the desert?

52 Jesus and the paralytic man
(Matthew 9:1-8; Mark 2:1-12; Luke 5:17-26)

Write the answer to each question.

1. Where was Jesus when the man was brought to him?

2. How many people were there?

3. Who was brought to Jesus?

4. In what town was Jesus when he met this man?

5. Why couldn't he get to Jesus?

6. How many friends were with him?

7. Where did they take the man?

8. How did they get their friend to Jesus?

9. When Jesus saw the man, what did he say?

10. Why did Jesus heal the man?

11. In their minds, what did the Pharisees accuse Jesus of?

12. How did Jesus answer them?

13. What did Jesus say to the man?

14. What did the man do?

15. How did the crowd react when they saw this?

53 Mary, Martha and Lazarus
(Luke 10:38–42; John 11:1–44)

Write the answer to each question.

1. Who were the two ladies involved in this story?

2. What was their relationship to each other?

3. What did Mary do?

4. What did Martha do?

5. What was Martha's reaction to Mary?

6. What did Jesus say?

7. Why is it important to sit still and listen?

8. How can we listen to God

9. What was the name of Mary and Martha's brother?

10. Where did Mary, Martha and Lazarus live?

11. When Jesus heard that Lazarus was sick, what did he do?

12. When Jesus saw how upset Mary and Martha were, what did he do?

13. When Jesus arrived at the tomb what did he do?

14. After he had prayed, what did he say?

15. What happened when Jesus called out to Lazarus?

54 'I am' sayings in John's Gospel

Write the answer to each question.

1. Who do the 'I am' sayings teach about?

2. To what did Jesus say he is the way?

3. Finish the verse: 'I am the way ...'

4. What were the disciples asking Jesus about when he answered, 'I am the way ...'?

5. How many ways are there to heaven?

6. What is the way to heaven?

7. Jesus said, 'I am the good ...'

8. Who are the sheep?

9. What sort of food did Jesus describe himself as?

10. What did Jesus mean when he said, 'I am the bread of life'?

11. Finish this sentence: 'I am the light ...'

12. Jesus said he was 'the _____ and the life'

13. Jesus said he was 'the true ...'

14. What else did Jesus say he was?

15. When Jesus used the phrase 'I am', what was he claiming?

55 The disciples

Write the answer to each question.

1. Name two of Jesus's disciples

2. What did Peter, Andrew, James and John do for a living?

3. Which disciple used to be a tax collector?

4. Which disciple walked on the water?

5. Which disciples were known as 'the sons of thunder'?

6. Which was the disciple Jesus especially loved?

7. Which disciple brought the small boy to Jesus with his lunch?

8. How many disciples met Jesus on the road to Emmaus?

9. Which disciple betrayed Jesus for thirty pieces of silver?

10. Which two disciples arrived at Jesus's tomb first?

11. Which disciple did Jesus ask to look after his mother?

12. Which disciple doubted Jesus's resurrection?

13. Which disciple preached on the day of Pentecost?

14. Which disciple went to find Nathanael to tell him about Jesus?

15. Which disciples were with Jesus at the transfiguration?

56 Occupations

Name the occupations of the following people:

1. David was a ...

2. Zacchaeus was a ...

3. Luke was a ...

4. Peter, James, John and Andrew were ...

5. Joseph (Mary's husband) was a ...

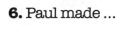

6. Paul made ...

7. Matthew was a ...

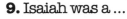

8. Herod was a ...

9. Isaiah was a ...

10. Samuel was a ...

11. Joshua was a ...

12. Esau was a ...

13. Ruth collected ...

14. Esther was a ...

15. Amos was a ...

57 Creatures in the Bible

Write the answer to each question.

1. In the baker's dream, what creatures took the bread from the basket?

2. What animal spoke to Balaam?

3. What creatures brought food to Elijah?

4. What animals did David kill to protect the sheep?

5. What did Samson kill with his bare hands?

6. What was Peter's job before he became a disciple of Jesus?

7. What creature brought back an olive leaf to Noah?

8. What creature rescued Jonah from the sea?

9. What animal came upon Jesus at his baptism?

10. What animal carried Jesus into Jerusalem?

11. What animal's hair was used to make John the Baptist's coat?

12. What creature tempted Eve in the garden?

13. What animal did the prodigal son care for?

14. What animals did Samson use to destroy the Philistine crops?

15. What creatures did God send as plagues on the Egyptians?

48 Mixed general—1

Write the answer to each question.

1. What was Luke's profession?

2. How did Stephen die?

3. Who held the coats of the people stoning Stephen

4. How old was Jesus when he was presented at the temple?

5. What did Stephen see when he looked up to heaven?

6. David looked after which animals?

7. What was David's father called?

8. What did the apostle Paul make?

9. James, Peter, John and Andrew were what?

10. What was wrong with Bartimaeus?

11. Which creatures brought food for Elijah?

12. Who prayed for a son?

13. How many books are there in the Old Testament

14. How many books are there in the New Testament

15. How many Commandments are there?

59 Mixed general—2

Write the answer to each question.

1. How many disciples did Jesus have?

2. Who betrayed Jesus?

3. Where was Jesus born?

4. What is the name of the fourth Gospel?

5. What did God send after the flood as a promise never to flood the earth again?

6. On what did Jesus ride into Jerusalem on Palm Sunday?

7. How many books are there in the Bible?

8. Name two of Jesus's disciples.

8. Name two books in the Bible.

10. What was Moses' sister called?

11. How many people were crucified with Jesus?

12. Name one of the Ten Commandments.

13. What was the name of the first woman?

14. Describe one of the miracles Jesus performed.

15. Name one of the parables Jesus told.

60 Mixed general—3

Write the answer to each question.

1. How many people were saved in the ark?

2. Name one of Noah's sons.

3. What was Samuel's mother called?

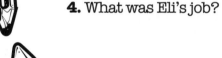

4. What was Eli's job?

5. What creature spoke to Eve in the garden?

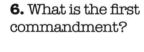

6. What is the first commandment?

7. What is the second commandment?

8. What did Daniel do at his window?

9. What happened to Daniel?

10. What was Samuel told to say when he was called?

11. What was Abraham's wife called?

12. Where was Jonah told to go and preach?

13. To where did Jonah run?

14. To what did Saul change his name?

15. How many stones did David use to kill Goliath?

61 Number puzzle

Write the missing words in each statement. The first
letter of each word is given as a clue.

1. Forty-nine y. between j.
(Leviticus 25:10)

2. Three t. P. d. J. (Matthew
26:69–75)

3. Three thousand b. at P. (Acts
2:1, 41)

4. Forty y. w. in the w.
(Numbers 32:13)

5. Six d. in c. (Genesis 1)

6. Seven s. and seven g. l.
(Revelation 1:20)

7. Four G. in the N. T.
(Matthew, Mark, Luke, John)

8. Seventy y. of c. in B.
(Jeremiah 29:10)

9. Ten p. on the l. of E. (Exodus
7–12)

10. One d. for one d.'s w.
(Matthew 20:2)

11. Fifty-two d. to r. the w. of J.
(Nehemiah 6:15)

12. Five l. and two f. f. five
thousand m. (Matthew
14:17–21)

13. Seven hundred w. and
three hundred c. of S. (1 Kings
11:3)

14. Three s. of N.: S., H. and J.
(Genesis 10:1)

15. Three d. witnessed J.'s t.
(Matthew 17:1–2)

```
Q E O H T S B U O O P
M I A R F R T L G W M
U L U N M A U J R D Y
O C E U O I P G A N V
A L M S D M K S P S R
H X O WORD A G S D
F J SEARCHES X
Q B N G O A U B O V A
S P A I M F Q L R S Y
H O S J R T G E I U C
C F K E B H P T L T X
```

62 Noah's ark

```
W A R F O R T Y H T R A E F P O H
A E A B M R A I N B O W O N L M U
A E M W B E E Q W F D E S T R O Y
L T W D G I H V S E C Y P R E S S
J O E N E A V S G M T D U Z W Q U
H E O V W K E P R A P R O M I S E
F A C K I L L J X L U C F L F D B
H A M N E L M A O E R I E D H D S
V Z M M E Q O F W R R V Y T T N U
J V A C G L S Y A D O A N Z E T O
D L L O D S O T D D C R I I H F E
B M E V N G L I N X L A G D P L T
M V Z E E A M H V Y C R H K A O H
K J V N I C A A J C K A T F J O G
W A T A A N I M A L A T S O G D I
R D U N C V H F S U R W I O Q E R
X Y P T M G V H F O K O D D Q D P
```

Altar	**Earth**	**Noah**
Animal	**Female**	**Olive**
Ararat	**Flooded**	**Promise**
Ark	**Food**	**Rainbow**
Blameless	**Forty**	**Raven**
Corrupt	**God**	**Righteous**
Covenant	**Ham**	**Shem**
Cypress	**Japheth**	**Two**
Days	**Leaf**	**Violence**
Destroy	**Male**	**Walked**
Dove	**Nights**	

63 Joseph's dreams

```
N Z G Z K M T R O P E R G D Y
P E Y T B R O T H E R S R A M
C R E H T A F V H E R T A B S
A X U T G S G A I D L Y I J O
N Q E B N J T G Z R O Q N I N
A U T J O E N A S E V A E H S
A S S N D W V D F A E Q B S W
N B O L Q Z E E F M D O H U H
S O Z R S S U D S P R V Z O P
M P J L H J S N T T R E O L F
H P E S O J J B A T U R G A F
D N O G D T A R R E B U K E D
Y V T C Y D C W S B G P R J R
R D H H T D O U P R I G H T N
B E C K F A B A S K C O L F X
```

Bad	**Hated**	**Report**
Bowed	**Jacob**	**Seventeen**
Brothers	**Jealous**	**Sheaves**
Canaan	**Joseph**	**Sons**
Dream	**Loved**	**Stars**
Father	**Moon**	**Sun**
Flocks	**Rebuked**	**Upright**
Grain	**Reign**	

64 The plagues of Egypt

```
F I R S T B O R N S O C S K C
T Y F L C M D M Z B B G C H P
S J Q L T W L K O I O O C A A
H U L D I J H E A R T O Z I S
U O Z M E E C M F S B O I L S
B H L L P H S Q E T Z Y L P O
S L A A R O N V S U Z K O H V
Y W O X J X I E M V S F C A E
F P X O F L S G G S H A U R R
P J N Y D O N U E Y W D S D B
L F X G M Y X N S P P W T E L
A G N A T S K D J F H T S N C
G I A H O R U X E G O S H E N
U N Y H A D E A T H N P F D R
E O K D P H A R A O H A T D Y
```

Aaron
Blood
Boils
Darkness
Death
Egypt
Firstborn

Flies
Frogs
Gnats
Goshen
Hail
Hardened
Heart

Livestock
Locusts
Moses
Passover
Pharaoh
Plague

65 Ruth

```
B E T H L E H E M W P P M
C V N N M A H L O N I J Z
Q P N A M S N I K R U F G
N E S E O Q J M R U T H E
T O T L T M A E I O B E D
S P I G G R I L S Y H T X
E L F L A B X E E E H S C
T E A U I D F C V L T E N
I Z V H X K N H A R R V O
B Y O A K I U P E A N R K
A P U P A L D X H B O A Z
O K R R G N I H S E R H T
M Q G O N R E M E E D E R
```

Barley	Kilion	People
Bethlehem	Kinsman	Redeemer
Boaz	Mahlon	Ruth
Elimelech	Mara	Sheaves
Favour	Moabite	Threshing
Glean	Naomi	Wife
Grain	Obed	
Harvest	Orpah	

66 David and Goliath

```
A D P N T E Z V L A V P Y W L I O
D N H D E S P I S E D W A G G S D
E U I E R E Q L O R D C H O X R E
L O L L R N R F J H N H Q L G A L
L R I Q I Z S E N O T S D I C E I
I G S U F Y I A D E I A S A U L V
K H T M I C H A C R Q G G T Z I E
Q T I B E I E A J Y T S B H E T R
L O N P D H O I F S I M N U D E E
O O E X E R E K D A O W X O E S D
U M S R O Y Z L B R O N Z E Y C U
F S O M B P R E H D T D G N A L E
Y F B G F T V U E T T D A N M U G
V O F B D I C C O H E Z K V S N U
H E B A F F A O G M I B P O I I A
G Q J X T F Z I K L R X M L D D K
A U E N C S F H C Q F A S V O P M
```

Armour	**Fight**	**Philistines**
Bethlehem	**Five**	**Saul**
Boy	**Forehead**	**Sling**
Bronze	**Gath**	**Smooth**
David	**Goliath**	**Staff**
Delivered	**Ground**	**Stones**
Despised	**Israelites**	**Terrified**
Dismayed	**Killed**	
Facedown	**Lord**	

67 The floating axehead

```
F E C L E H G D S L N
L Z P E H A E S E O S
O E R A R W T I R W O
A T S E O W Z I V N P
T J O R D A N A A E R
U T R G O T Z X N L O
B O S H P E W E T I P
B Q A T G R E H S S H
C U T T I N G E R H E
E W C Y E C Q A S A T
L O R D V R K D U H S
```

Axehead	Iron	Stick
Borrowed	Jordan	Tree
Cutting	Lord	Water
Elisha	Prophets	
Float	Servants	

68 Esther

```
I K V C V Z T S A C K C L O T H W R V
W C N E P E D I E V T Z S C E P T R E
C E Y W U A H F U D S P U R I M C T X
L S U Q E I K U W W C T M N F S O R E
V Y N N S A X M O M H E T K N E N E R
V A O L U A L L D S U S A K I O S A X
B I H P U C L T W R A T X W I D P T E
A B R E N A H T H F D H I T Y Y I M S
S B D G G J E S O Q H E A M J R R E B
S N E E I A E N V B J R S O U O A N S
A P K A P N I O U E B M H R Y T C T A
S A F M U O S N H E L H E D J R Y S O
S Y Q I T T S Y L A E A S E N S V I H
I T E H V L I E N C D M D C A B U S X
N N N D F A C F D Y Z A Q A D L J P S
A I S L I R S N U Y W N S I J E W S G
T N A U L C T H S L X G S S V K S J A
E H B I P V T P T H Q E U S A Z E C T
G S J Y P F J K K I N G D O M H Q G L
```

Ashes	Fast	Sackcloth
Assassinate	Gallows	Sceptre
Banquet	Hadassah	Susa
Beautiful	Half	Treatments
Celebration	Haman	Vashti
Conspiracy	Hegai	Virgins
Deposed	Jews	Wealth
Edict	Kingdom	Xerxes
Esther	Mordecai	
Eunuchs	Purim	

69 Fiery furnace

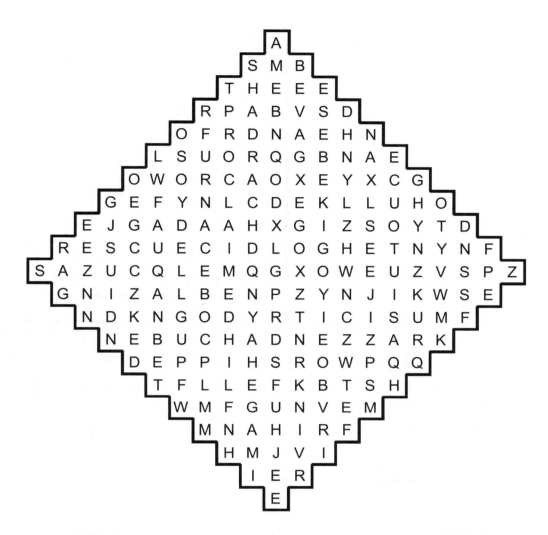

```
                    A
                  S M B
                T H E E E
              R P A B V S D
            O F R D N A E H N
          L S U O R Q G B N A E
        O W O R C A O X E Y X C G
      G E F Y N L C D E K L L U H O
    E J G A D A A H X G I Z S O Y T D
  R E S C U E C I D L O G H E T N Y N F
S A Z U C Q L E M Q G X O W E U Z V S P Z
  G N I Z A L B E N P Z Y N J I K W S E
    N D K N G O D Y R T I C I S U M F
      N E B U C H A D N E Z Z A R K
        D E P P I H S R O W P Q Q
          T F L L E F K B T S H
            W M F G U N V E M
              M N A H I R F
                H M J V I
                  I E R
                    E
```

Abednego	**God**	**Proclaimed**
Angels	**Gold**	**Rescue**
Astrologers	**Image**	**Serve**
Babylon	**Jews**	**Seven**
Blazing	**Meshach**	**Shadrach**
Fire	**Music**	**Worshipped**
Four	**Nebuchadnezzar**	
Furnace	**Ninety**	

70 Jonah

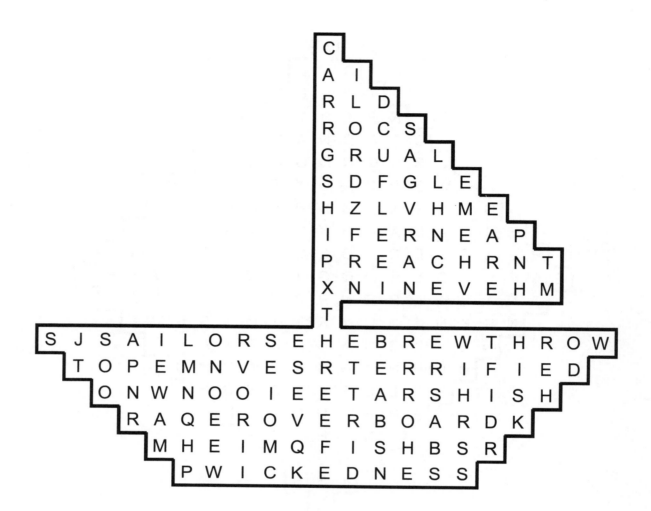

	Calm		Overboard		Storm
	Fish		Perish		Tarshish
	Flee		Preach		Terrified
	God		Ran		Three
	Hebrew		Rougher		Throw
	Jonah		Sailors		Wickedness
	Lord		Ship		
	Nineveh		Sleep		

'71 Christmas

Angels
Baby
Bethlehem
Caesar
Census
Cloths

David
Decree
Dream
Firstborn
Flocks
Frankincense

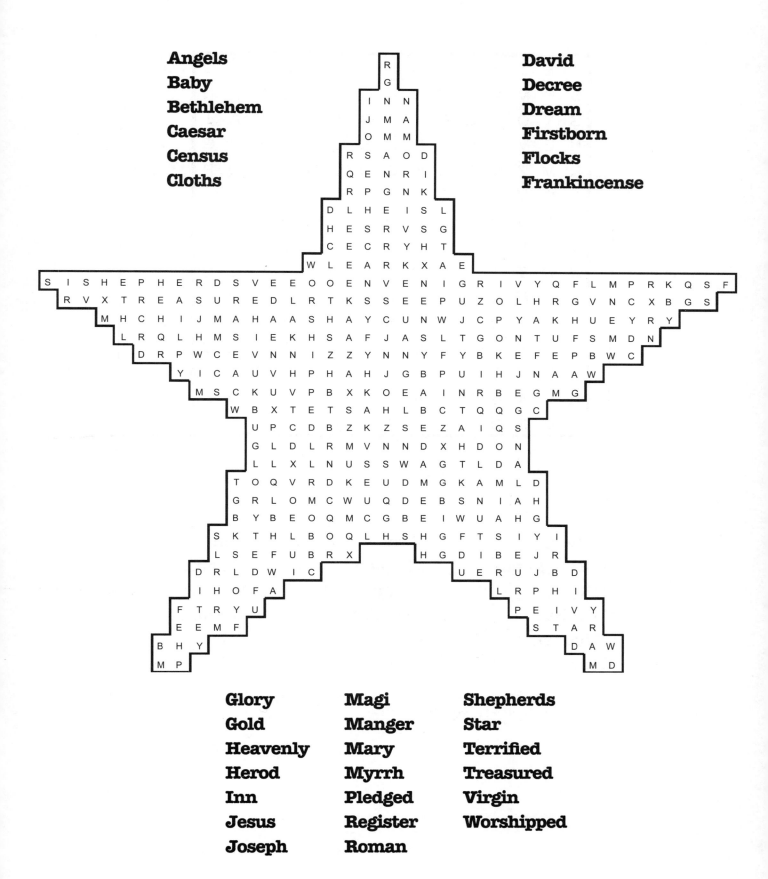

Glory
Gold
Heavenly
Herod
Inn
Jesus
Joseph

Magi
Manger
Mary
Myrrh
Pledged
Register
Roman

Shepherds
Star
Terrified
Treasured
Virgin
Worshipped

72 The parable of the ten virgins

```
G E I X G K M M U C E R W J S
S P M A L N W U Q O D B N Z N
G Y Q Y G F I Y Q T F A L A I
N E V A E H E D H O E V Y B G
R M Z M T E N G D W M T R Q R
X O V G V B I T H E F U W M I
Z Y S H S N R O L O W H P O V
M W F M D E Y I O A U S E D E
W W T I O M R L D H P R E G H
A M M K F Y I X Y E G A L N Q
T C T D Q S Y N G J G J S I V
C B H T H K O O M L C R A K U
H R C C K L I G Y D M G O R M
G J A B P L A G Q W I S E O S
M J R O S O R D L K K Z C C M
```

Asleep   Jars   Ten
Bridegroom   Kingdom   Virgins
Day   Lamps   Watch
Foolish   Midnight   Wedding
Heaven   Oil   Wise
Hour   Shut

73 The parable of the mustard seed

```
O B T U C Y E Z Z F H
Z P L A N T E D H E Q
S L K E D H R A G Y N
M C A C S D R I B C Q
A P A R A B L E P D D
L L W L G R O W S R N
L V X L W E G J A K U
E W Q U M L S T H B O
S J Z P G V S T J T R
T X Z E L U S E E D G
C E E Q M B A K G Q B
```

Birds   **Largest**   **Planted**
Ground   **Mustard**   **Seed**
Grows   **Parable**   **Smallest**

74 The parable of the prodigal son

```
D R K U O K N G S C D V P
E F X C H R N I N H F R U
Y B F F E I A E E S O N S
O S Z E R N B F F D H E E
U B J E F O M Z I A W D S
N P I D R T L G N O S M G
G M N I B C A X R H A W J
E B R N M L X T P V Y L R
R G N G Y B H N S R G E R
Y E N O M Y C N G B H N N
X Z X G F A F N E T Y I S
A L I V E W U F A W S W Q
O W T Q L H P F D K X S U
```

Alive	**Neck**	**Sons**
Far	**Prodigal**	**Swine**
Father	**Ring**	**Two**
Feeding	**Robe**	**Worthy**
Hungry	**Safe**	**Younger**
Money	**Shoes**	

75 The parable of the wise and foolish builders

```
S D M T G I S O P Q L
T Y N A O D N F L S U
R Z B A N O G E T R D
E L R I S Z H L K A O
A Q W I Q S C L C E M
M J N V I R T R O H E
S W R L A P A L R S T
C N O I B S M D I C I
W O N R H H U W Q U X
F O U N D A T I O N B
M H H O U S E W R Y J
```

Built   Hears   Streams
Crash   House   Winds
Fell   Rain   Wise
Foolish   Rock   Words
Foundation   Sand

'76 Zacchaeus

```
C C Z A C C H A E U S L V J O T V
S N O I S S E S S O P H D V E P Q
S Y J Q G A B Q E E J E W F G T I
A T F B Z Y N A V N T K P P Q I E
M Y A U H Y Y L D A L G O R C X G
B L I Y H E K R E P Q H M S D Q C
P E J O X J P H Z Y C Z W E E Z M
S T S O L W C A C I E R K A B E P
A A R U O F M U R O R O Z A M W K
L I R U S S G E P J O Z Z L I E X
V D D W R H J M S L M M J F L L K
A E G E T Q O E V S A V E C C C X
T M U A R F D R S U C G W D C O Y
I M U L E L O E T U Y F M L V M D
O I L T E O A C U W S Q Z Z M E L
N J I H P S I U E O F B D S K D J
M F O Y T A X C O L L E C T O R H
```

Cheated	Lost	Sycamore
Climbed	Poor	Tax collector
Four	Possessions	Tree
Gladly	Salvation	Wealthy
Immediately	Save	Welcomed
Jericho	Seek	Zacchaeus
Jesus	Short	
Looked	Stay	

77 He is risen

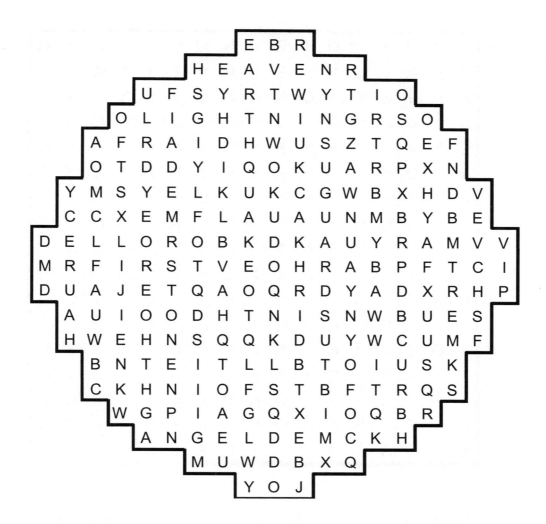

```
          E B R
        H E A V E N R
      U F S Y R T W Y T I O
      O L I G H T N I N G R S O
      A F R A I D H W U S Z T Q E F
      O T D D Y I Q O K U A R P X N
    Y M S Y E L K U K C G W B X H D V
    C C X E M F L A U A U N M B Y B E
  D E L L O R O B K D K A U Y R A M V V
  M R F I R S T V E O H R A B P F T C I
  D U A J E T Q A O Q R D Y A D X R H P
  A U I O O D H T N I S N W B U E S
  H W E H N S Q Q K D U Y W C U M F
    B N T E I T L L B T O I U S K
    C K H N I O F S T B F T R Q S
      W G P I A G Q X I O Q B R
      A N G E L D E M C K H
        M U W D B X Q
          Y O J
```

Afraid	**First**	**Risen**
Angel	**Go**	**Rolled**
Crucified	**Guards**	**Sabbath**
Dawn	**Heaven**	**Shook**
Day	**Joy**	**Stone**
Dead	**Lightning**	**Tomb**
Earthquake	**Mary**	

78 Philip and the Ethiopian eunuch

```
B V M I G O I E U N U C H V G P G
F S R V O Y L B S H R Z T N W Q V
K P J S S I Q N W D G Y I Y R V H
S I U N P F I J P Y J D S E G O D
C R X Y E A Y E V P A M T U F E Q
W I D H L Y E R S E F H L K Z X I
E T F P X H G U R Q G Z T I C V S
P T X D S I Q S R U V R T O Q U A
R E H G E S W A A C Y P W J H S I
O F F I C I A L X C A N D A C E A
P A C U O P S E A B G K H U T C H
H W A H G P G M H M W A V R M E V
E O J M A K I N A S B C J Q Q S R
T I M P O R T A N T W O R S H I P
J E S U S P I U N D E R S T A N D
O Y Z Y N D Q O N P H I L I P F U
W C T S C R I P T U R E Q G A Z A
```

Baptized	Important	Reading
Candace	Isaiah	Scripture
Chariot	Jerusalem	Sheep
Ethiopian	Jesus	Slaughter
Eunuch	Lamb	Spirit
Explains	Official	Understand
Gaza	Philip	Water
Gospel	Prophet	Worship

Saul's conversion

```
S Y N A G O G U E S S Y D B D H J
S O E Y X O Q M U H V G A W H U W
P L A M V U F S Q M N I M T E P R
E W H P I W E M A I T I A F A E R
E N N Y K J B U Y R A K S L V W F
C E P Y W R H A H M M F C P E R R
H E O J E N R K T F Z Z U S N E T
L B S F S P O C B A K M S F A H P
E D F F J E R U S A L E M N G U K
S U B A P T I Z E D L V O I T K L
S F W C N L N E W I X I A B H P T
F F G G I A O S T W S R O K R J R
B B M B I L N N M I T T R M E H L
C L H J D I E I V S P K T P A U L
V J I Y Y G I A A U F G I L T I U
R U D N Q H P R I S O N E R S O Q
V P A I D T K V P E R S E C U T E
```

Ananias	Jesus	Speechless
Baptized	Light	Straight
Blind	Paul	Suffer
Damascus	Persecute	Synagogues
Gentiles	Praying	Threats
Heaven	Prisoners	Vision
Jerusalem	Saul	Way

80 Books of the Old Testament

```
I S H A B A K K U K N U M B E R S
A G A L A M E N T A T I O N S L U
G N I A H A I M E R E J C S J D H
G O R L E M F C D P U M U U E A A
A S A E C S Z X A L Y D D U I E Q
H F H I M L O I N H O G T M C S L
D O C N A V G H A X E E E C S E M
L G E A L W P I E S R H L B V U K
E N Z D A V N Z G O E E R I H I S
I O A K C A M E N N S E T A N S M
K S R S H A N O J I V I N G O A L
E Y Z P I E M G A O C V S B R Y A
Z Q E J S Y W S R U T H A A Y L S
E Z O I V Z T P S V W D M G I Q P
H E S T J E I M J I I O D J O A G
L A U H S O J I V A S A M U E L H
E S T H E R B C H R O N I C L E S
```

Amos	**Genesis**	**Joshua**	**Numbers**
Chronicles	**Habakkuk**	**Judges**	**Obadiah**
Daniel	**Haggai**	**Kings**	**Proverbs**
Deuteronomy	**Hosea**	**Lamentations**	**Psalms**
Ecclesiastes	**Isaiah**	**Leviticus**	**Ruth**
Esther	**Jeremiah**	**Malachi**	**Samuel**
Exodus	**Job**	**Micah**	**Song of Songs**
Ezekiel	**Joel**	**Nahum**	**Zechariah**
Ezra	**Jonah**	**Nehemiah**	**Zephaniah**

81 Books of the New Testament

```
R M S N A I T A L A G V U N I
W D Q V Z D S M F G W A C T S
R B U F G U G S N A M O R G E
C O R I N T H I A N S D E G K
Y T L N D A U E O L H G T S U
J F I F O T N E D U J Z E N L
S E S N A I P P I L I H P A T
N W P S N N T E Z T F D J I Y
M K E H U Z H A M T N A S S H
A O X R E A G O L L M K U S T
T W Y P B S D W J E R M T O O
T C P Z N E I G S A V M I L M
H S R H V S H A M Z M E T O I
E P H I L E M O N G T B R C T
W S N A I N O L A S S E H T D
```

Acts	**John**	**Philippians**
Colossians	**Jude**	**Revelation**
Corinthians	**Luke**	**Romans**
Ephesians	**Mark**	**Thessalonians**
Galatians	**Matthew**	**Timothy**
Hebrews	**Peter**	**Titus**
James	**Philemon**	

TRUE ☑ OR FALSE? ☒

82 Creation

Write T for true or F for false in the square to the
right of each question on the chess board.

1. God only created only the heavens and the earth.

2. When God saw the light, he said it was good.

3. God called the darkness Day.

4. God created Heaven on the second day.

5. On the third day, God made animals.

6. God did not like the birds and fish he created.

7. God did not want the birds and fish to increase in number.

8. Man is made in the image of God.

9. God made Adam out of Eve's rib.

10. God was pleased with his creation.

11. God rested on the seventh day.

12. God made Adam to be a helper for Eve.

13. God breathed life into Adam.

14. God made the sun and moon on the fourth day.

15. God created the world in seven days.

83 Genesis 1-4

Write T for true or F for false in the square to the right of each question on the chess board.

1. In the beginning God created the heavens and earth.		**2.** Jesus existed in heaven before he came to earth as a baby.		**3.** Cain killed his brother Abel because Abel was better looking.	
	4. God created the world in seven days.		**5.** God made man from the water.		
6. God made woman from a rib.		**7.** The first man was Adam.		**8.** The first woman was Hannah.	
	9. Adam and Eve had three sons: Cain, Abel and Seth.		**10.** Abel worked in the fields.		
11. Eve was tempted by a lizard.		**12.** Adam and Eve hid from God.		**13.** God walked with Adam and Eve.	
	14. There was a tree in the garden called the tree of information.		**15.** A flaming sword guarded the way to the tree of life after Adam and Eve were banished.		

84 Noah

Write T for true or F for false in the square to the right of each question on the chess board.

1. God saw the earth had become wicked so decided to destroy it.		**2.** Noah was righteous and blameless.		**3.** The best place to read the story of Noah is in the Book of Exodus.	
	4. Noah got his plans for the ark from God.		**5.** Noah was 600 years old when the flood began.		
6. Noah and his wife had four sons.		**7.** Noah cared for vineyards.		**8.** Noah took four of every type of animal into the ark.	
	9. When Noah and his family were in the ark it rained for forty days and forty nights.		**10.** Noah sent out a raven to see if there was dry ground anywhere.		
11. The raven brought back an olive branch.		**12.** An ark is an old work of art.		**13.** When he got out of the ark, the first thing Noah did was have a party.	
	14. God sent thunder as a promise that he would never flood the earth again.		**15.** God has kept his promise.		

85 The twelve tribes of Israel

Write T for true or F for false in the square to the right of each question on the chess board.

1. Benjamin was not one of Jacob's sons.		**2.** The Levites' inheritance was the priesthood.		**3.** Jesus was from the tribe of Simeon.	
	4. Naphtali is one of the twelve tribes		**5.** Israel was Jacob's other name.		
6. David was from the tribe of Judah.		**7.** When the twelve tribes conquered Canaan they were to drive out the current occupants.		8. The tribes completed their task of conquest against Canaan.	
	9. James wrote a letter to the scattered twelve tribes.		**10.** Judah is often referred to as a lamb.		
11. Esther was a Benjamite.		**12.** God was one of the twelve tribes.		**13.** Moses was a Levite.	
	14. Ruth was from the tribe of Judah.		**15.** The twelve tribes of Israel were mostly named after Jacob's twelve sons.		

86 Samson

Write T for true or F for false in the square to the right of each question on the chess board.

1. Samson's father was Manoah.		**2.** Samson was from the tribe of Zebulun.		**3.** Samson's mother was told by an angel about Samson.	
	4. Not to eat pork is an important part of the Nazirite vow.		**5.** Samson was not allowed to cut his hair.		
6. Samson killed a lion on his way to Timnah.		**7.** Samson ate honey from an animal carcass.		**8.** Samson never told Delilah the secret to his strength.	
	9. Samson lost his strength by drinking wine.		**10.** Samson killed more people in his death than in his life.		
11. The story of Samson is found in Deuteronomy.		**12.** Samson was blinded by the Philistines.		**13.** Samson's mum and dad wanted him to marry an Israelite.	
	14. Samson led the people for fifteen years.		**15.** Samson died when the temple came crashing down.		

87 David

Write T for true or F for false in the square to the right of each question on the chess board.

1. David looked after cows.		**2.** David's father was Jesse.		**3.** David was the youngest in his family.			
	4. David's family were from Nazareth.		**5.** Samuel asked Jesse to gather all his sons together.				
6. God sent Samuel to David's house.		**7.** David was the first son Samuel met.		**8.** David was to become king.			
	9. Samuel anointed David with blood.		**10.** David wrote Psalm 23.				
11. Saul tried to kill David.		**12.** David was one of Jesus's anscestors.		**13.** David's best friend was Joshua.			
	14. David fought Goliath.		**15.** David was married to Abigail.				

Write T for true or F for false in the square to the right of each question on the chess board.

1. Zechariah was a priest.		**2.** Zechariah was married to Anna.	**3.** Zechariah went into the temple to burn incense.
	4. The angel told Zechariah he was to have a daughter.	**5.** Zechariah did not believe the angel at first.	
6. Zechariah was struck blind because he did not believe the angel.		**7.** Elizabeth was Mary's relative.	**8.** Zechariah said that the baby was to be called John.
	9. When Mary met Elizabeth, the baby in Elizabeth's womb leapt for joy.	**10.** Zechariah never spoke again.	
11. Zechariah was chosen by lot to go into the temple.		**12.** The angel appeared standing on the left of the altar.	**13.** Zechariah doubted the angel because he was too old.
	14. The people realized that Zechariah had seen a vision when he could not talk.	**15.** Zechariah gradually learnt how to speak again.	

89 Christmas

Write T for true or F for false in the square to the right of each question on the chess board.

1. Joseph was Jesus's true father.		**2.** Jesus was born in Bethlehem.				**3.** The wise men were three kings from the orient.	
	4. Herod was really excited when he heard that a new king had been born.			**5.** A prophet in the Old Testament wrote about where Christ would be born.			
6. God warned the wise men in a dream that they should not return to Herod.		**7.** The wise men ignored God's warning and went back to Herod anyway.				**8.** Joseph and Mary went to Bethlehem because of a decree by Caesar Augustus.	
	9. Mary and Joseph fled to Israel after Jesus was born.			**10.** Jesus was born in an inn.			
11. Quirinius was governor of Syria at the time Caesar Augustus's decree was issued.		**12.** Joseph went to Bethlehem because he was in the line of Moses.				**13.** An angel of the Lord appeared to some shepherds.	
	14. The shepherds decided not to bother to go and visit the baby			**15.** The angels were praising God.			

90 Jesus

Write T for true or F for false in the square to the right of each question on the chess board.

1. Jesus had fourteen disciples.		**2.** Simon Peter betrayed Jesus to the Jewish leaders.		**3.** Jesus was crucified.	
	4. Jesus taught his disciples the Prayer of Peace.		**5.** Jesus fed the 6,000 with loaves and fish.		
6. The Pharisees liked to try to trap Jesus with questions.		**7.** Jesus's mother was Mary.		**8.** Jesus's stories were called miracles.	
	9. After Jesus rose from the dead, he ascended into heaven.		**10.** The Bible says that Jesus never cried.		
11. Jesus performed many parables.		**12.** Jesus had a half-brother called James.		**13.** Mary and Martha were close friends of Jesus.	
	14. Jesus sometimes preached from a plane.		**15.** Jesus's followers deserted him when he was arrested.		

91 Parables

Write T for true or F for false in the square to the right of each question on the chess board.

1. In the Parable of the Good Samaritan, it was the priest who helped the injured man.

2. When the prodigal son returned, his father asked for his ring back.

3. The kingdom of heaven is described as hidden treasure.

4. The ten virgins did not take enough oil.

5. The foolish man built his house on a rock.

6. When a fig tree starts producing leaves, you know that winter is near.

7. A man gave his three servants five, ten and fifteen talents.

8. In the Parable of the Sower, Jesus says, 'He who has feet, let him walk.'

9. The Old Testament prophesied that Jesus would talk in parables.

10. The best thing to do with a lit lamp is to hide it under the bed.

11. Jesus spoke about a broad and a narrow path.

12. Jesus said that the kingdom of heaven is like a mustard seed.

13. In the Parable of the Lost Coin, Jesus said that the angels rejoice over a sinner who repents.

14. Jesus told parables about a lost son, coin, sheep and dog.

15. When telling parables, Jesus often used the things he saw around him.

92 Jesus's resurrection

Write T for true or F for false in the square to the right of each question on the chess board.

1. Mary Magdalene saw Christ on the day of his resurrection.		**2.** An earthquake accompanied the resurrection.		**3.** The women rolled away the stone from the tomb.	
	4. An angel informed the women that Christ would go to Galilee.		**5.** Peter outran the other disciple on their way to the tomb.		
6. Thomas believed in Jesus's resurrection when he saw the fish.		**7.** Mary did not know Jesus when she first saw him.		**8.** The guards ran to tell the Romans what had happened.	
	9. The Romans claimed that the disciples had stolen the body of Jesus at night.		**10.** Emmaus is about ten miles from Jerusalem.		
11. The two on the Emmaus road didn't recognize Jesus immediately.		**12.** Jesus appeared to the disciples, Thomas being absent, on the first day of the week.		**13.** The resurrected body of Jesus could appear through locked doors.	
	14. The women visited the tomb at dusk.		**15.** Jesus preached to the two disciples on the road to Emmaus.		

93 Paul's missionary journeys

Write T for true or F for false in the square to the right of each question on the chess board.

1. John Mark was Paul's first travelling companion.

2. Paul was stoned at Lystra.

3. At Iconium, lots of people believed the message, which made the Jews happy.

4. Paul healed a blind man in Lystra.

5. Paul and Barnabas argued over John Mark.

6. Barnabas was mistaken for the god Zeus.

7. Paul and Timothy were thrown into prison for healing a fortune-telling girl.

8. A Philippian jailor was converted during an earthquake.

9. Paul went on three missionary journeys.

10. Paul was keen to go to Rome, but kept being stopped.

11. Paul used to be called Saul.

12. Paul took different people with him on his missionary journeys.

13. Paul was welcomed in every city he entered.

14. Paul was thrown into prison on some of his journeys.

15. Paul travelled in Asia on his journeys.

94 The epistles

Write T for true or F for false in the square to the right of each question on the chess board.

1. When Peter wrote his second letter, he thought he had at least twenty years left to live.		**2.** Mark and Luke sent greetings at the end of Paul's letter to Philemon?		**3. Timothy** learnt about faith through watching his father.
	4. Paul wanted to preach to people who had never heard the gospel before.		**5.** The church in Corinth was full of problems.	
6. Peter was a married man.		**7.** In Thessalonians Paul teaches that Christ will come again.		**8.** In Philippians Paul teaches it is important to dwell on all the negative things in the world.
	9. Paul had just been released from prison when he wrote Colossians.		**10.** Paul writes about Onesimus in Philemon.	
11. Paul was in prison when he wrote Philippians.		**12.** Hebrews lists the men and women of faith.		**13.** Titus lived in Athens.
	14. When Paul wrote to the Romans he had just returned from visiting them.		**15.** Paul wrote two letters to the Thessalonians.	

95 Books of the Bible

Write T for true or F for false in the square to the right of each question on the chess board.

1. The Book of Hezekiah is in the Old Testament.

2. Luke wrote the Acts of the Apostles.

3. Peter wrote three letters.

4. The Pentateuch is the first four books of the Old Testament.

5. Three Bible books are named after women.

6. Paul write Romans.

7. There are five Gospels.

8. There are twenty-seven books in the New Testament.

9. There are sixty-seven books in the Bible.

10. Jeremiah wrote Lamentations.

11. Exodus tells the story of Moses.

12. Genesis means 'beginnings'.

13. John wrote six books in the New Testament.

14. The book of Acts is about the life of Jesus.

15. Proverbs is a book of wisdom.

96 Cities

Write T for true or F for false in the square to the right of each question on the chess board.

1. Jesus was born in Bethlehem.		**2.** In the story of the Good Samaritan, the injured man was travelling to Jerusalem.		**3.** Mary, Martha and Lazarus were from Bethany.	
	4. Jesus's first miracle took place in Cana.		**5.** David was first anointed to be king at Eden.		
6. God destroyed Sodom because it was a wicked city.		**7.** Abraham came from Ur.		**8.** Paul's hometown was Tarsus.	
	9. Daniel was exiled to Syria.		**10.** Jonah went to preach in Joppa.		
11. Paul was travelling to Damascus when he met Jesus.		**12.** Moses ran away from Pharaoh to Jerusalem.		**13.** Nehemiah was in Susa when news reached him about Jerusalem.	
	14. Samson was from Dan.		**15.** Paul wrote a letter to people living in Ephesus.		

97 Food and drink

Write T for true or F for false in the square to the right of each question on the chess board.

1. Esau sold his birthright for stew.		**2.** The land promised to the Israelites was flowing with milk and wine.	**3.** Timothy was advised to take a little wine for his stomach.
	4. Jesus turned wine into water.	**5.** Simon Peter ate locusts and honey.	
6. Jesus fed 4,000 with loaves and fish.	**7.** Daniel ate only vegetables for ten days.	**8.** The devil tempted Jesus to turn stones into bread in the wilderness.	
	9. Nehemiah's job was to check that the king's wine wasn't poisoned.	**10.** Jesus asked for sour wine when he was on the cross.	
11. The twelve spies who went to Canaan brought back bunches of grapes.	**12.** Elijah was fed by ravens.		**13.** Xerxes threw a banquet in Esther's honour.
	14. Jesus told a parable about a fig-tree.	**15.** The Old Testament Israelites were not allowed to eat shellfish.	

98 Geography

Write T for true or F for false in the square to the right of each question on the chess board.

1. The disciples and Christ were on Mount Olivet when Jesus ascended into heaven.		**2.** Peter and John were going to church when they saw the man who was lame from birth.	**3.** Abraham's father died in Nineveh.
	4. Philip went to Samaria to preach the gospel.	**5.** Saul was going to Damascus when he met Jesus on the road and was blinded.	
6. After Saul's conversion, he preached first in Damascus and then he went to Bethany.	**7.** Peter healed a paralysed man named Aeneas at Lystra.	**8.** Dorcas was raised from the dead in Jericho.	
9. Peter came from Galilee.	**10.** The disciples were first called Christians in Asia.		
11. God confused the language of the people at the tower of Babel.	**12.** Abraham moved to Ur because God told him to.	**13.** Mary and Joseph took Jesus to Egypt when he was a baby.	
14. God parted the Red Sea.	**15.** Paul met Ananias at Straight Street.		

99 Mixed Old Testament

Write T for true or F for false in the square to the right of each question on the chess board.

1. Noah had eight sons.

2. Daniel prayed at least three times a day.

3. Joseph had a wife called Potiphar.

4. Joseph's brother stole from him.

5. Joseph's brothers sold him into slavery.

6. 'You shall have no other gods before me' is the first commandment.

7. Cain killed Abel.

8. Moses' brother was called Aaron.

9. Hannah had a baby called Eli.

10. God created the world in six days.

11. Jonah was swallowed by a goldfish.

12. Jeremiah was thrown into a well.

13. Esau had a twin.

14. All the psalms were written by David.

15. Zechariah is the last book in the Old Testament.

100 Mixed New Testament

Write T for true or F for false in the square to the right of each question on the chess board.

1. Jesus said, 'I am the Good Shepherd.'

2. Jesus was born in Nazareth.

3. Jesus rode a horse into Jerusalem.

4. Peter's other name was Simon.

5. Revelation is the last book in the Bible.

6. Jesus said, 'I am the Gate'.

7. Paul changed his name to Saul.

8. Jesus had eleven disciples.

9. John wrote five books in the New Testament.

10. Mary Magdalene was the mother of Jesus.

11. Judas Iscariot betrayed Jesus for three pieces of silver.

12. Acts was written to Theophilus.

13. Matthias was the disciple chosen to replace Judas.

14. Paul met Jesus on the road to Samaria.

15. The 'armour of God' passage is found in Galatians.

101 Mixed Old and New Testament

Write T for true or F for false in the square to the right of each question on the chess board.

1. The multitude cried 'Hosanna!' to Jesus when he entered Jerusalem.

2. Elisha cast his mantle upon Elijah.

3. The last word in the book of Revelation is Amen.

4. Christ's twelve disciples were also called epistles.

5. Paul testified to the Jews that Jesus was the Christ.

6. Cain never married.

7. Dogs licked up Ahab's blood.

8. Achan was killed in the Valley of Achor.

9. Mephibosheth was the lame son of Jonathan.

10. Michal, King Saul's daughter, loved David.

11. The first name in the Bible is God.

12. Solomon had many wives.

13. Hezekiah is the fourteenth book in the Bible.

14. The first five books of the Bible are called the Pentateuch.

15. The Beatitudes are found in the book of Acts.

Answers

Codebreakers

1 Genesis 1:31

2 Joshua 1:9

3 Psalm 4:3

4 Proverbs 3:5

5 Jonah 2:2

6 Jonah 4:2

7 Mark 16:6

8 Mark 16:15

9 Luke 12:34

10 John 3:16

11 John 14:6

12 Acts 3:19

13 Acts 4:12

14 Romans 10:9

15 Ephesians 6:10–11

16 Philippians 2:11

17 Philippians 4:19

18 1 Thessalonians 5:16–18

19 1 Timothy 1:15

20 1 John 4:4

Crosswords

21 The Ten Commandments

22 The golden calf (Exod. 32)

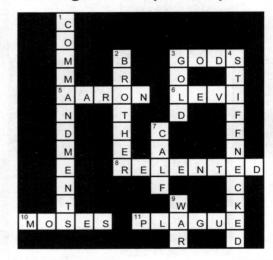

23 The twelve tribes of Israel

24 The call of Gideon (Judg. 6:11–40)

25 Psalm 23

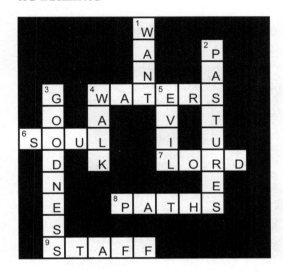

26 Jonah

27 People in the Old Testament

28 Christmas (Matt. 1–2; Luke 2)

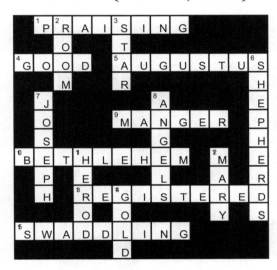

29 The baptism of Jesus (Matt. 3:13–17)

30 The little children and Jesus (Mark 10:13–16)

31 The feeding of the five thousand (Matt. 14:13–21)

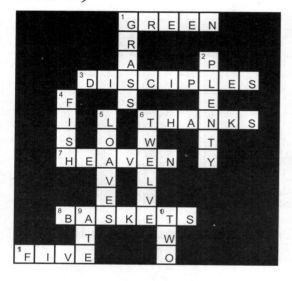

32 Jesus calms the storm (Luke 8:22–25)

33 Jesus betrayed (Mark 14:43–52)

34 Peter denies Jesus (Matt. 26:69–75; Luke 22:54–62)

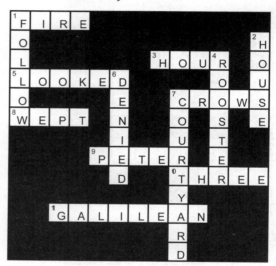

35 Jesus's death and resurrection

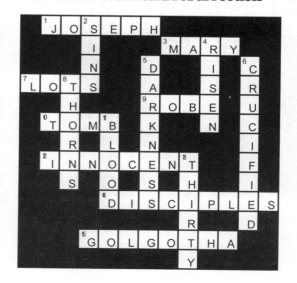

36 The Gospels

37 The armour of God (Eph. 6:10-18)

38 The letter to Philemon

39 The letters to the seven churches (Rev. 2-3)

40 Mothers in the Bible

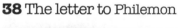

Questions and answers

41 Creation (Genesis 1-2)
1   Light and darkness
2   Sky and water
3   Dry land and plants
4   Sun, moon and stars
5   Fish and birds
6   Animals and man
7   He rested
8   Adam
9   A special friend for Adam
10 Eve
11 One of Adam's ribs
12 A garden
13 Eden
14 Dust on the ground
15 He breathed into him

42 The Fall (Genesis 3)
1   Live together, have children and work in the garden
2   Tree of life / tree of the knowledge of good and evil
3   Tree of the knowledge of good and evil / tree of life
4   You are free to eat from any tree in the garden; but you must not eat from the tree of the knowledge of good and evil, for when you eat of it you will surely die
5   Serpent
6   The devil
7   Did God really tell you not to eat from any tree?
8   She took fruit from the tree of the knowledge of good and evil, and ate it and offered some to Adam
9   Ran and hid because they were ashamed
10 Clothes out of leaves
11 The woman you put here with me gave me some fruit from the tree and I ate it
12 Clothes out of animal skins
13 He was angry
14 They were sent away from the garden
15 He sent Jesus

43 Cain and Abel (Genesis 4:1-17)
1   Cain and Abel
2   Farmer
3   Shepherd
4   A lamb
5   Vegetables
6   Abel's
7   He was angry
8   Go into the field with him
9   Killed Abel
10 Where is Abel?
11 Am I my brother's keeper?
12 A mark
13 The land of Nod
14 Enoch
15 His son

44 Noah (Genesis 6-9)
1   Because of their wickedness
2   Noah
3   Ham, Shem and Japheth
4   Forty days and forty nights
5   600
6   Eight
7   A pair of each
8   He shut the door
9   150 days
10 Mount Ararat
11 A raven
12 A dove
13 An olive leaf
14 He built an altar
15 A rainbow

45 Abraham and Lot (Genesis 13-14)
1   Desert
2   Rich
3   Uncle and nephew
4   That they go separate ways
5   Lot
6   Sodom
7   To the mountains
8   Wicked
9   No
10 Other kings
11 He went to help
12 318
13 Back to Sodom
14 Melchizedek
15 A tenth

46 Joseph—the early years (Genesis 37)
1   Jacob
2   Rachel
3   She died giving birth to Benjamin
4   Eleven brothers and one sister
5   Joseph
6   A coat of many colours
7   They hated him
8   His brother's sheaves of corn bowing down to his
9   That they would have to bow down to him one day
10 The sun, moon and stars bowing down to him
11 That Joseph's father and mother would also bow down to him
12 Kill him
13 Reuben
14 Put him in a dry well
15 Midianite traders

47 Job
1   Uz

2 As blameless and upright
3 Satan
4 Job himself
5 One
6 Kill him
7 Boils
8 His wife
9 Eliphaz, Bildad and Zophar
10 Seven days and seven nights
11 They saw how great his suffering was
12 Out of a storm
13 Job
14 Made him prosperous again
15 Pieces of silver and gold rings

48 Jonah

1 Nineveh
2 Joppa
3 Tarshish
4 There was a great storm
5 They cried out to their gods
6 To throw him overboard
7 Three days and three nights
8 He prayed
9 The fish vomited him up onto dry land
10 He told him a second time to go to Nineveh
11 That in forty days Nineveh would be overturned
12 They repented
13 He sulked
14 A vine
15 A worm ate it

49 The prophets

1 Uzziah
2 Seventy years
3 Priest
4 Nebuchadnezzar
5 Gomer
6 Locusts
7 A famine of hearing God's Word
8 Edom
9 Bethlehem
10 Nineveh
11 Babylon
12 Repent and turn to God
13 The temple
14 Four
15 Paying tithes and offerings

50 Jesus's childhood (Luke 2:41–52)

1 Mary and Joseph
2 God
3 He was a carpenter
4 Nazareth
5 Egypt
6 Twelve
7 For the Passover feast
8 One day
9 Three days
10 In the temple
11 Speaking with the temple teachers
12 They were amazed at his understanding
13 Didn't you know I would be in my Father's house?
14 He was obedient to his parents and grew in wisdom.
15 She treasured in her heart all the things that had happened

51 Jesus's baptism and temptation (Matthew 3:13–4:11; Mark 1:9–13; Luke 3:21–23; 4:1–13)

1 John the Baptist
2 You need to baptize me
3 Dove
4 The Holy Spirit
5 This is my Son whom I love; with him I am well pleased.
6 Camel's-hair tunic
7 Locusts and wild honey
8 The river Jordan
9 They were related
10 To fulfil all righteousness
11 Into the desert
12 Forty days and forty nights
13 He was tempted
14 The Scriptures
15 Angels

52 Jesus and the paralytic man (Matthew 9:1–8; Mark 2:1–12; Luke 5:17–26)

1 In a house
2 Lots and lots
3 A man who couldn't walk
4 Capernaum
5 It was too crowded
6 Four
7 Onto the roof
8 They lowered him through the roof
9 Your sins are forgiven
10 To show that he had the power to forgive sin
11 Blasphemy
12 He asked, 'Which is easier: to say to someone that his or her sins are forgiven, or to heal that person?'
13 Take up your bed and walk
14 He got up, took up his mat and walked home, praising God
15 They were amazed

53 Mary, Martha and Lazarus (Luke 10:38-42; John 11:1-44)

1. Martha and Mary
2. They were sisters
3. Sat still and listened to Jesus
4. Rushed around making preparations
5. She got cross and asked Jesus to tell her to help
6. That Mary had chosen the better way
7. It is the best way to learn
8. Through prayer, reading the Bible and listening to teaching
9. Lazarus
10. Bethany
11. He stayed where he was two more days
12. He wept
13. He prayed
14. 'Lazarus, come out!'
15. Lazarus came out of the tomb—alive!

54 'I am' sayings in John's Gospel

1. Jesus
2. Eternal life
3. … the truth and the life
4. The way to heaven
5. One
6. Jesus
7. Shepherd
8. We are
9. Bread
10. That he is everything a person could need
11. … of the world
12. Resurrection
13. Vine
14. The gate
15. That he was God

55 The disciples

1. Simon Peter, Andrew, James, John, Judas, Matthew, Thomas, Philip, Bartholomew (also known as Nathanael), James, Simon, Thaddaeus
2. They were fishermen
3. Matthew
4. Peter
5. James and John
6. John
7. Andrew
8. Two
9. Judas Iscariot
10. Peter and John
11. John
12. Thomas
13. Peter
14. Philip
15. Peter, James and John

56 Occupations

1. Shepherd
2. Tax collector
3. Doctor
4. Fishermen
5. Carpenter
6. Tents
7. Tax collector
8. King
9. Prophet
10. Judge
11. Warrior
12. Hunter
13. Wheat and barley
14. Queen
15. Shepherd

57 Creatures in the Bible

1. Birds
2. Donkey
3. Ravens
4. Lion and bear
5. Lion
6. Fisherman
7. Dove
8. Big fish
9. Dove
10. Colt
11. Camel
12. Serpent
13. Pigs
14. Foxes
15. Frogs and gnats

58 Mixed general—1

1. Doctor
2. He was stoned
3. Saul
4. Eight days
5. A vision of Jesus
6. Sheep
7. Jesse
8. Tents
9. Fishermen
10. He was blind
11. Ravens
12. Hannah
13. Thirty-nine
14. Twenty-seven
15. Ten

59 Mixed general—2

1. Twelve
2. Judas Iscariot
3. Bethlehem
4. John
5. A rainbow
6. Colt
7. Sixty-six
8. Two of Jesus's disciples.
9. Two books in the Bible.
10. Miriam
11. Two
12. One of the Ten Commandments.
13. Eve
14. One of the miracles Jesus performed.
15. One of the parables Jesus told.

60 Mixed general—3

1. Eight
2. Shem, Ham or Japheth
3. Hannah
4. Priest

5 Serpent
6 You shall have no other gods before me
7 Do not make an idol
8 He prayed
9 He was thrown into lions' den
10 Speak, Lord, for your servant is listening
11 Sarah
12 Nineveh
13 Tarshish
14 Paul
15 One

61 Number puzzle

1 Forty-nine years between jubilees
2 Three times Peter denied Jesus
3 Three thousand baptized at Pentecost
4 Forty years wandering in the wilderness
5 Six days in creation
6 Seven stars and seven golden lampstands
7 Four Gospels in the New Testament
8 Seventy years of captivity in Babylon
9 Ten plagues on the land of Egypt
10 One denarius for one day's work
11 Ffity-two days to rebuild the walls of Jerusalem
12 Five loaves and two fish fed five thousand men
13 Seven hundred wives and three hundred concubines of Solomon
14 Three sons of Noah: Shem, Ham and Japheth
15 Three disciples witnessed Jesus's transfiguration

Wordsearches

62 Noah's ark

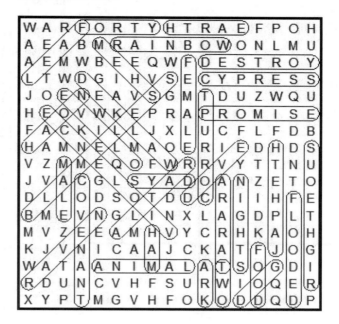

63 Joseph's dreams

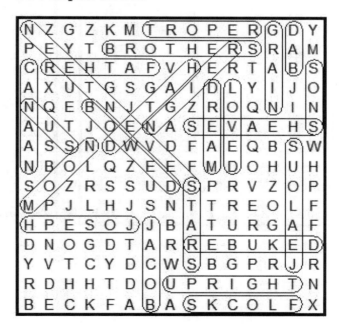

64 The plagues of Egypt

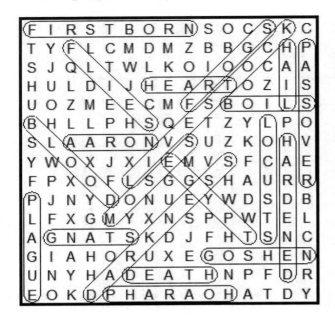

66 David and Goliath

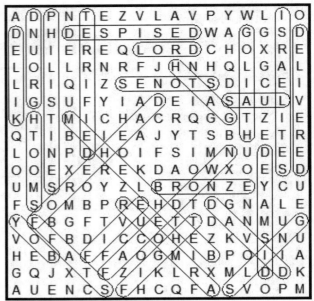

65 Ruth

67 The floating axehead

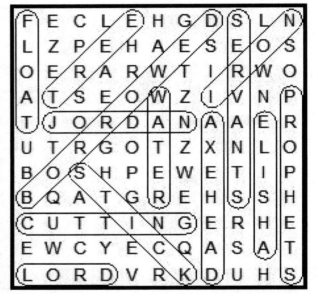

68 Esther

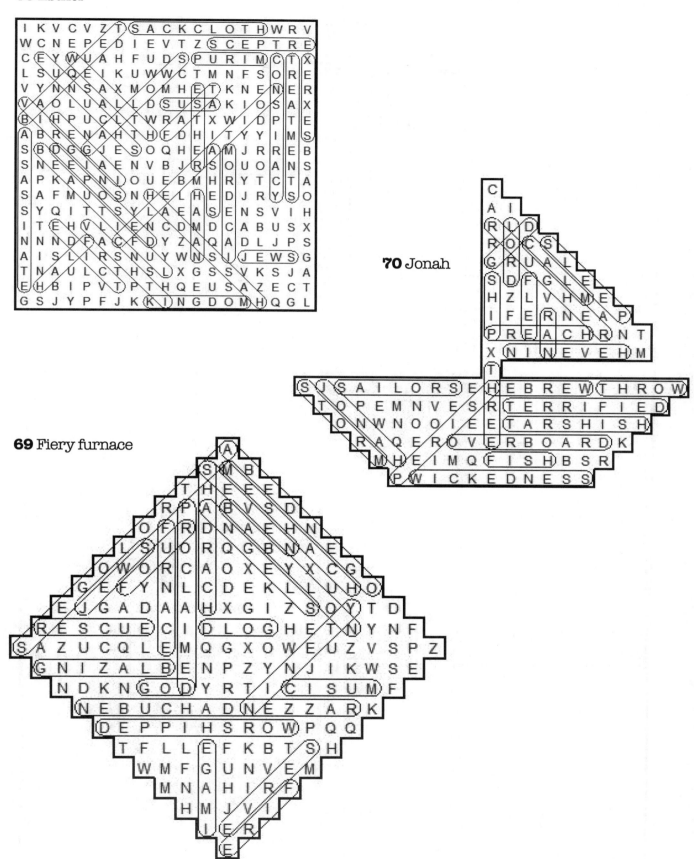

69 Fiery furnace

70 Jonah

71 Christmas

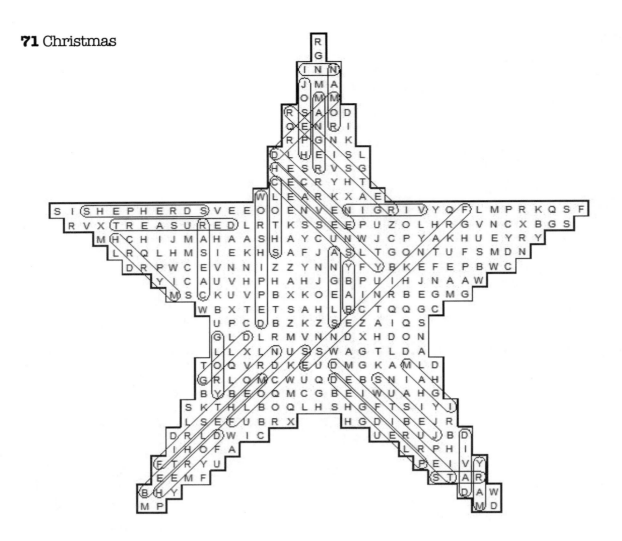

72 The Parable of the Ten Virgins

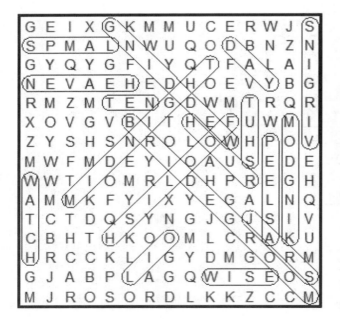

73 The Parable of the Mustard Seed

74 The Parable of the Prodigal Son

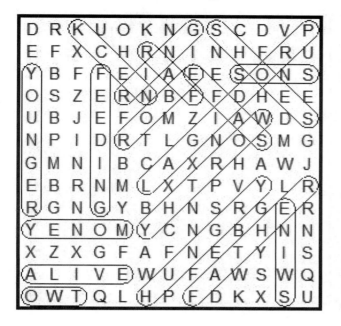

76 Zacchaeus

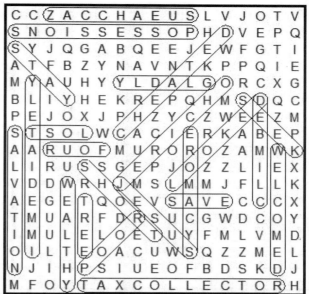

75 The Parable of the Wise and Foolish Builders

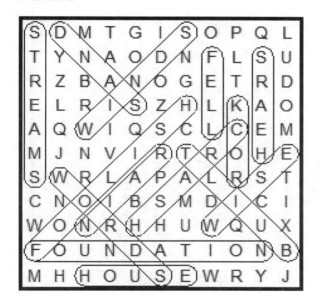

77 He is risen!

78 Philip and the Ethiopian eunuch

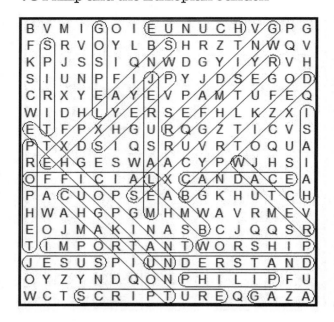

80 Books of the Old Testament

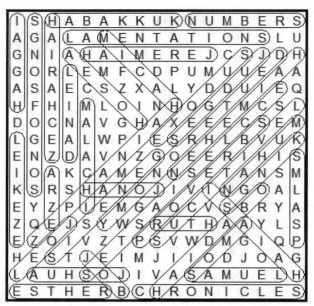

79 Saul's conversion

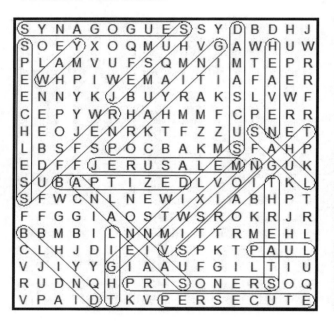

81 Books of the New Testament

True or false?

82 Creation

1 False
2 True
3 False
4 True
5 False
6 False
7 False
8 True
9 False
10 True
11 True
12 False
13 True
14 True
15 False

83 Genesis 1–4

1 True
2 True
3 False
4 False
5 False
6 True
7 True
8 False
9 True
10 False
11 False
12 True
13 True
14 False
15 True

84 Noah

1 True
2 True
3 False
4 True
5 True
6 False
7 True
8 False
9 True
10 True
11 False
12 False

13 False
14 False
15 True

85 The twelve tribes of Israel

1 False
2 True
3 False
4 True
5 True
6 True
7 True
8 False
9 True
10 False
11 True
12 False
13 True
14 False
15 True

86 Samson

1 True
2 False
3 True
4 False
5 True
6 True
7 True
8 False
9 False
10 True
11 False
12 True
13 True
14 False
15 True

87 David

1 False
2 True
3 True
4 False
5 True
6 True
7 False
8 True
9 False

10 True
11 True
12 True
13 False
14 True
15 True

88 Zechariah

1 True
2 False
3 True
4 False
5 True
6 False
7 True
8 True
9 True
10 False
11 True
12 False
13 True
14 True
15 False

89 Christmas

1 False
2 True
3 False
4 False
5 True
6 True
7 False
8 True
9 False
10 False
11 True
12 False
13 True
14 False
15 True

90 Jesus

1 False
2 False
3 True
4 False
5 False
6 True
7 True

8 False
9 True
10 False
11 False
12 True
13 True
14 False
15 True

91 Parables

1 False
2 False
3 True
4 True
5 False
6 False
7 False
8 False
9 True
10 False
11 True
12 True
13 True
14 False
15 True

92 Jesus's resurrection

1 True
2 True
3 False
4 False
5 False
6 False
7 True
8 False
9 True
10 False
11 True
12 True
13 True
14 False
15 True

93 Paul's missionary journeys

1 False
2 True
3 False

4 False
5 True
6 True
7 False
8 True
9 True
10 True
11 True
12 True
13 False
14 True
15 True

94 The epistles

1 False
2 True
3 False
4 True
5 True
6 True
7 True
8 False
9 False
10 True
11 True
12 True
13 False
14 False
15 True

95 Books of the Bible

1 False
2 True
3 True
4 False
5 False
6 True
7 False
8 True
9 False
10 True
11 True
12 True
13 False
14 False
15 True

96 Cities

1 True

2 False
3 True
4 True
5 False
6 True
7 True
8 True
9 False
10 False
11 True
12 False
13 True
14 True
15 True

97 Food and drink

1 True
2 False
3 True
4 False
5 False
6 True
7 True
8 True
9 True
10 False
11 True
12 True
13 False
14 True
15 True

98 Geography

1 True
2 False
3 False
4 True
5 True
6 False
7 False
8 False
9 True
10 False
11 True
12 False
13 True
14 True
15 True

99 Mixed Old Testament

1 False
2 True
3 False
4 False
5 True
6 True
7 True
8 True
9 False
10 True
11 False
12 True
13 True
14 False
15 False

100 Mixed New Testament

1 True
2 False
3 False
4 True
5 True
6 True
7 False
8 False
9 True
10 False
11 False
12 True
13 True
14 False
15 False

101 Mixed Old and New Testament

1 True
2 False
3 True
4 False
5 True
6 False
7 True
8 True
9 True
10 True
11 True

12 True
13 False
14 True
15 False

120 Great
Orientalist Paintings

CD-ROM & Book

Edited by
Carol Belanger Grafton

Dover Publications, Inc.
Mineola, New York

The CD-ROM in this book contains all of the images. Each image has been saved as a high-resolution JPEG and an Internet-ready JPEG. There is no installation necessary. Just insert the CD into your computer and call the images into your favorite software (refer to the documentation with your software for further instructions).

Within the "Images" folder on the CD you will find two additional folders—"High Resolution JPG" and "JPG." Every image has a unique file name in the following format: xxx.JPG. The first 3 characters of the file name correspond to the number printed with the image in the book. The last 3 letters of the file name, JPG, refer to the file format. So, 001.JPG would be the first file in the folder.

Also included on the CD-ROM is Dover Design Manager, a simple graphics editing program for Windows that will allow you to view, print, crop, and rotate the images.

For technical support, contact:
Telephone: 1 (617) 249-0245
Fax: 1 (617) 249-0245
Email: dover@artimaging.com
Internet: **http://www.dovertechsupport.com**
The fastest way to receive technical support is via email or the Internet.

Bibliographical Note

120 Great Orientalist Paintings CD-ROM & Book is a new selection of images, first published by Dover Publications, Inc., in 2009.

Dover Electronic Clip Art®

International Standard Book Number
ISBN-13: 978-0-486-99038-5
ISBN-10: 0-486-99038-9

Manufactured in the United States by Courier Corporation
99038901
www.doverpublications.com

001. WILLIAM ALLAN
Slave Market in Constantinople; 1838

002. GIUSEPPE ANGELELLI
The Franco-Tuscan Expedition in the Ruins of Thebes; c. 1836

004. CHARLES BARGUE
A Bashi-Bazouk; 1875

003. JACQUES AVED
*Portrait of the Pasha Mehmed Said, Bey of Rovurelia, Ambassador of
Sultan Mahmud I at Versailles*; 1742

006. GUSTAV BAUERNFEIND
Ruined Temple in Baalbeck; 1882

005. CHARLES BARGUE
Arab Dealer Among His Antiques; 1877

007. GUSTAV BAUERNFEIND
Market in Jaffa; 1887

008. FRÉDÉRIC BAZILLE
The Toilette; 1869–1870

009. LÉON BELLY
Pilgrims Going to Mecca; 1861

010. LÉON BELLY
The Stranded Dahbieh; 1877

011. JEAN-JOSEPH BENJAMIN CONSTANT
The Entry of Mahomet II into Constantinople; 1876

012. LÉON BENOUVILLE
Esther; 1844

013. ÉMILE BERNARD
Woman Smoking Hashish (or *Woman Smoking a Tombac*); 1900

014. LÉON BONNAT
The Barber of Suez; 1876

015. PAUL-LOUIS BOUCHARD
Après le bain; c. 1894

016. FREDERICK ARTHUR BRIDGMAN
The Siesta (Afternoon in Dreams); 1878

017. FREDERICK ARTHUR BRIDGMAN
The Courtyard; 1873

018. FREDERICK ARTHUR BRIDGMAN
The Game of Chance; 1885

020. FREDERICK ARTHUR BRIDGMAN
The Day of the Prophet at Oued-el-Kebir; [n.d.]

021. APPOLODORE CALLET
The Embarkation of the Inhabitants of Parga; 1827

022. JOHN CARLIN
The New Captive; 1876

024. THÉODORE CHASSÉRIAU
The Caliph of Constantine, Ali-Hamed, Chief of the Hrakta,
Followed by His Escort; 1845

023. THÉODORE CHASSÉRIAU
Harem Interior; 1854

025. THÉODORE CHASSÉRIAU
Arab Horsemen Reclaiming Their Dead; 1850

026. FREDERIC EDWIN CHURCH
Syria by the Sea; 1873

028. Léon Comerre
Les Coquelicots; [n.d.]

027. Félix-Auguste Clément
Women Selling Water and Oranges on the Road to Heliopolis, Near Cairo; 1872

030. ADRIEN DAUZATS
Mosque of Al Azhar in Cairo; 1831

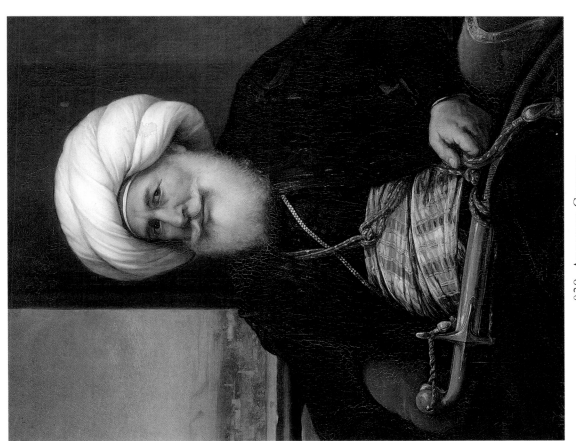

029. AUGUSTE COUDER
Muhammad Ali, Viceroy of Egypt; 1840

032. EDOUARD DEBAT-PONSON
The Daughter of Jephthas; 1876

033. Alexandre-Gabriel Decamps
The Punishment of the Hooks; 1837

034. Alfred Dehodencq
Dance of the Blacks in Tangier; 1874

035. Eugène Delacroix
The Death of Sardanapalus; 1827

036. Eugène Delacroix
Turk Seated on a Sofa and Smoking; 1825

037. Eugène Delacroix
The Fanatics of Tangier; 1838

038. Eugène Delacroix
Algerian Women in Their Apartments; 1834

040. Ludwig Deutsch
A Palace Guard; 1892

039. Eugène Delacroix
*Mulay Abd al-Rahman, Sultan of Morocco, Leaving His Palace in Meknes,
Surrounded by his Guard and his Chief Officers; 1845*

041. Narcisse de la Peña
Oriental Woman and Her Daughter; 1865

042. Sir Frank Dicksee
Leila; 1892

043. CHARLES DUFRESNE
Patio in Algiers; 1912

044. RUDOLF ERNST
Femmes filant au Maroc; [n.d.]

045. Rudolf Ernst
The Hookah Smoker; [n.d.]

046. James Fairman
Sunset; [n.d.]

047. ANTOINE DE FAVRAY
Turkish Women; c. 1754

048. HENRY FERGUSON
Mosque of Sultan Hassan; Cairo [n.d.]

049. Ludwig Hans Fischer
The Simoom; [n.d.]

050. Auguste de Forbin
View of Jerusalem near the Valley of Jehoshaphat; 1825

051. MARIANO FORTUNY
The Café of the Swallows; 1868

052. EUGÈNE FROMENTIN
The Heron Hunt (Algeria); 1865

054. Eugène Fromentin
A Street in El-Aghouat; 1859

053. Eugène Fromentin
Arab Falconer; 1863

056. JEAN-LÉON GÉRÔME
Le Muezzin, the Call to Prayer; 1865

055. JEAN-LÉON GÉRÔME
The Carpet Merchant; c. 1887

057. Jean-Léon Gérôme
The Whirling Dervishes; 1899

058. Jean-Léon Gérôme
Interior of a Mosque; 1870

059. JEAN-LÉON GÉRÔME
Pool in a Harem; 1876

060. JEAN-LÉON GÉRÔME
A Café in Cairo; c. 1883

062. CHARLES GLEYRE
Woman of the Orient; 1840

061. NICOLAOS GHYZIS
The Slave Market; 1873–1875

063. FREDERICK GOODALL
A New Attraction in the Harem; [n.d.]

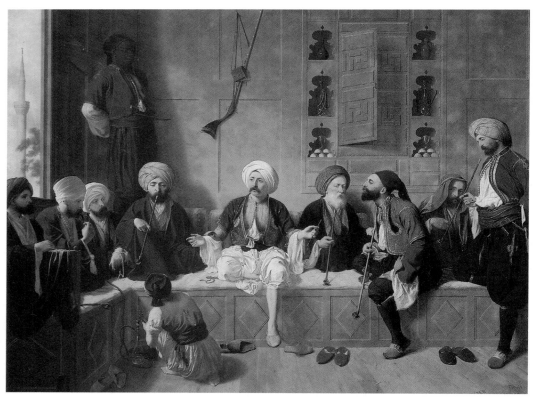

064. WALTER GOULD
An Eastern Story Teller; 1871

065. WALTER GOULD
The Public Scribe; 1869

066. ANTOINE-JEAN GROS
Portrait of Doctor Clot-Bey; 1833

067. Pierre Narcisse Guérin
Bonaparte Pardoning the Insurgents in Cairo (23 October 1798); 1808

068. Gustave Guillamet
Ain Kerma (Spring of the Fig Trees), Smalah of Tiaret in Algeria; 1867

070. OSMAN HAMDY-BEY
Old Man in Front of a Child's Tomb; 1903

069. CARL HAAG
Portrait of Jane Digby el Mezrab (Palmyra); 1859

071. Thomas Hicks
Bayard Taylor with a View of Damascus; 1855

072. Jean-August-Dominique Ingres
Odalisque with Slave; 1839

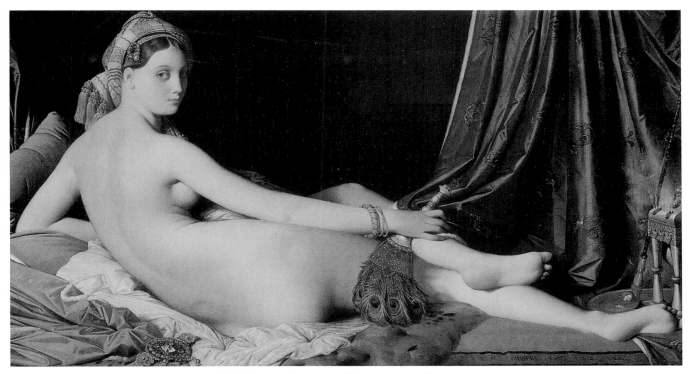

073. JEAN-AUGUST-DOMINIQUE INGRES
La Grande Odalisque; 1814

074. CHARLES LANDELLE
Female Fellah; [n.d.]

076. ROBERT SCOTT LAUDER
David Roberts Esq. in the Dress He Wore in Palestine; 1840

075. CHARLES LANDELLE
Jewish Girl in Tangiers; [n.d.]

078. JULES LAURENS
Ruins of the Palace of Asraf; [n.d.]

077. JULES LAURENS
Beginning of a Roman Road in Bithynia; 1896

080. Jean Lecomte de Noüy
The White Slave; 1888

079. Albert Lebourg
A Street in Algiers; 1875

082. JEAN LECOMTE DE NOÜY
The Dream of Khosru; 1874

083. FREDERICK, LORD LEIGHTON
The Light of the Hareem; c. 1880

084. FRANÇOIS-GABRIEL LÉPAULLE
The Pasha and his Harem; [n.d.]

086. JOHN FREDERICK LEWIS
Harem Life in Constantinople; c. 1857

085. HENRI-LÉOPOLD LÉVY
Bonaparte in the Great Mosque of Cairo; c. 1890

087. JOHN FREDERICK LEWIS
The Midday Meal, Cairo; 1875

088. JEAN ÉTIENNE LIOTARD
A Frankish Woman and Her Servant; c. 1750

089. JEAN ÉTIENNE LIOTARD
Portrait of M. Levett and of Mlle Glavany Seated on a Sofa; [n.d.]

090. WILLIAM LOGSDAIL
The Gates of Khalif; 1887

091. Vincenzo Marinelli
The Dance of the Bee in the Harem; 1862

092. Peder Mønsted
Portrait of a Nubian; [n.d.]

093. GUSTAVE MOREAU
Cleopatra; c. 1887

094. HENRY SIDDONS MOWBRAY
The Harem; c. 1885

095. CHARLES SPRAGUE PEARCE
The Death of the First-Born; 1877

096. HENRY WILLIAM PICKERSGILL
*Portrait of James Silk Buckingham and his Wife
in Arab Costume of 1816 of Baghdad; 1816*

098. Henri Regnault
*Summary Judgment Under the Moorish Kings
of Granada; 1870*

097. Sir Edward John Poynter
Young Girl Feeding the Sacred Ibises in the Hypostyle Room at Karnak; 1871

099. PIERRE-AUGUSTE RENOIR
Woman of Algiers, or, Odalisque; 1870

100. PIERRE-AUGUSTE RENOIR
Arab Festival in Algiers. The Casbah; 1881

102. Jean-André Rixens
Death of Cleopatra; 1874

104. DAVID ROBERTS
The Gateway to the Great Temple at Baalbek; 1841

103. DAVID ROBERTS
The Gate of Metwaley, Cairo; 1843

105. HENRI ROUSSEAU
Sleeping Gypsy; 1897

106. JOHN SINGER SARGENT
Fumée d'ambre gris (Tangiers); 1880

107. GEORGE L. SEYMOUR
A Consecration of Arms; [n.d.]

108. GUSTAVO SIMONI
The Halt of the Caravan; 1885

110. ANGE TISSIER
Algerian Woman and Her Slave, 1860

109. CHARLES JAMES THERIAT
The Vegetable Seller, 1895

111. JAMES TISSOT
Journey of the Magi; c. 1894

112. JAMES TISSOT
Sojourn in Egypt; 1886–1894

114. PAUL-DÉSIRÉ TROUILLEBERT
The Harem Servant; 1874

113. VIRGILIO TOJETTI
The Harem Dancer; [n.d.]

116. Eᴌɪʜᴜ Vᴇᴅᴅᴇʀ
Egyptian Tomb at Moonlight; [n.d.]

115. Eᴌɪʜᴜ Vᴇᴅᴅᴇʀ
The Questioner of the Sphinx; 1863

117. HORACE VERNET
The Massacre of the Mamelukes at the Citadel of Cairo; 1819

118. HORACE VERNET
Judah and Tamar; 1840

120. WILLIAM CLARK WONTNER
Safie, One of the Three Ladies of Bagdad; 1900

119. ÉLISABETH VIGÉE-LEBRUN
Madame Grassini in the Role of Zaire; c. 1805

LIST OF WORKS

001. William Allan (1782–1850); *Slave Market in Constantinople;* 1838; oil on canvas; 50¾" x 78" (129 x 198 cm)

002. Giuseppe Angelelli [n.d.]; *The Franco-Tuscan Expedition in the Ruins of Thebes;* c. 1836; oil on canvas; 90½" x 136⅝" (230 x 347 cm)

003. Jacques Aved (1702–1766); *Portrait of the Pasha Mehmed Said, Bey of Rovurelia, Ambassador of Sultan Mahmud I at Versailles;* 1742; oil on canvas; 93⅝" x 63⅜" (238 x 161 cm)

004. Charles Bargue (c. 1826–1883); *A Bashi-Bazouk;* 1875; oil on canvas; 18¼" x 13⅛" (46.4 x 33.3 cm)

005. Charles Bargue (c. 1826–1883); *Arab Dealer Among His Antiques;* 1877; oil on cradled panel. 13" x 9⅝" (33 x 24.5 cm)

006. Gustav Bauernfeind (1848–1904); *Ruined Temple in Baalbeck;* 1882; oil on canvas; 33½" x 20⅞" (85 x 53 cm)

007. Gustav Bauernfeind (1848–1904); *Market in Jaffa;* 1887; oil on canvas; 32¼" x 43" (82 x 109.2 cm)

008. Frédéric Bazille (1841–1870); *The Toilette;* 1869–1870; oil on canvas; 52" x 50" (132 x 127 cm)

009. Léon Belly (1827–1877); *Pilgrims Going to Mecca;* 1861; oil on canvas; 63⅜" x 95¼" (161 x 242 cm)

010. Léon Belly (1827–1877); *The Stranded Dahbieh;* 1877; oil on canvas; 43⅜" x 60½" (110.1 x 153.6 cm)

011. Jean-Joseph Benjamin Constant (1845–1902); *The Entry of Mahomet II into Constantinople;* 1876; oil on canvas; 274⅜" x 210" (697 x 536 cm)

012. Léon Benouville (1821–1859); *Esther;* 1844; oil on canvas; 48⅞" x 63¾" (124 x 162 cm)

013. Émile Bernard (1868–1941); *Woman Smoking Hashish* (or *Woman Smoking a Tombac*); 1900; oil on canvas; 33⅞" x 44½" (86 x 113 cm)

014. Léon Bonnat (1833–1922); *The Barber of Suez;* 1876; oil on canvas; 31½" x 23" (80 x 58.5 cm)

015. Paul-Louis Bouchard (1853–1937); *Après le bain;* c. 1894; oil on canvas; 86⅝" x 63" (220 x 160 cm)

016. Frederick Arthur Bridgman (1847–1928); *The Siesta (Afternoon in Dreams);* 1878; oil on canvas; 11¼" x 17" (28.5 x 43 cm)

017. Frederick Arthur Bridgman (1847–1928); *The Courtyard;* 1873; oil on canvas; 31½" x 41" (80 x 104 cm)

018. Frederick Arthur Bridgman (1847–1928); *The Game of Chance;* 1885; oil on canvas; 29½" x 39¾" (74.9 x 100.9 cm)

019. Frederick Arthur Bridgman (1847–1928); *Portrait of a Kabylie Woman, Algeria;* 1875; oil on canvas; 28½" x 23" (72.4 x 58.4 cm)

020. Frederick Arthur Bridgman (1847–1928); *The Day of the Prophet at Oued-el-Kebir;* [n.d.]; oil on canvas; 59⅝" x 78½" (150 x 200 cm)

021. Appolodore Callet (1799–1831); *The Embarkation of the Inhabitants of Parga;* 1827; oil on canvas; 148⅞" x 157⅞" (378 x 401 cm)

022. John Carlin (1813–1891); *The New Captive;* 1876; oil on canvas; 14¼" x 12" (36¼ x 30½ cm)

023. Théodore Chassériau (1819–1856); *Harem Interior;* 1854; oil on canvas; 26⅜" x 21⅝" (67 x 55 cm)

024. Théodore Chassériau (1819–1856); *The Caliph of Constantine, Ali-Hamed, Chief of the Hrakta, Followed by His Escort;* 1845; oil on canvas; 102⅜" x 128" (260 x 325 cm)

025. Théodore Chassériau (1819–1856); *Arab Horsemen Reclaiming Their Dead;* 1850; oil on canvas; 65¾" x 97⅝" (167 x 248 cm)

026. Frederic Edwin Church (1826–1900); *Syria by the Sea;* 1873; oil on canvas; 56" x 85" (142.2 x 215.9 cm)

027. Félix-Auguste Clément (1826–1888); *Women Selling Water and Oranges on the Road to Heliopolis, Near Cairo;* 1872; oil on canvas; 72⅞" x 48" (185 x 122 cm)

028. Léon Comerre (1850–1916); *Les Coquelicots;* [n.d.]; oil on canvas; 49" x 31⅛" (124.5 x 79 cm)

029. Auguste Couder (1790–1873); *Muhammad Ali, Viceroy of Egypt;* 1840; oil on canvas; 36⅝" x 29⅞" (93 x 76 cm)

030. Adrien Dauzats (1804–1868); *Mosque of Al Azhar in Cairo;* 1831; oil on canvas; 39⅜" x 31½" (100 x 80 cm)

031. Adrien Dauzats (1804–1868); *Fountain near the Mosque of Sultan Hassan in Cairo;* 1863; oil on wood. 25⅜" x 18⅞" (64.6 x 48 cm)

032. Edouard Debat-Ponson (1847–1913); *The Daughter of Jephthas;* 1876; oil on canvas; 51⅛" x 78" (130 x 198 cm)

033. Alexandre-Gabriel Decamps (1803–1860); *The Punishment of the Hooks;* 1837; oil on canvas; 35⅞" x 53⅞" (91 x 137 cm)

034. Alfred Dehodencq (1822–1882); *Dance of the Blacks in Tangier;* 1874; oil on canvas; 59⅞" x 79½" (152 x 202 cm)

035. Eugène Delacroix (1798–1863); *The Death of Sardanapalus;* 1827; oil on canvas; 154⅜" x 195¼" (392 x 496 cm)

036. Eugène Delacroix (1798–1863); *Turk Seated on a Sofa and Smoking;* 1825; oil on canvas; 9⅞" x 11¾" (25 x 30 cm)

037. Eugène Delacroix (1798–1863); *The Fanatics of Tangier;* 1838; oil on canvas; 38⅝" x 51⅝" (98 x 131 cm)

038. Eugène Delacroix (1798–1863); *Algerian Women in Their Apartments;* 1834; oil on canvas; 70⅞" x 90⅛" (180 x 229 cm)

039. Eugène Delacroix (1798–1863); *Mulay Abd al-Rahman, Sultan of Morocco, Leaving His Palace in Meknes, Surrounded by his Guard and his Chief Officers;* 1845; oil on canvas; 148½" x 133⅞" (377 x 340 cm)

040. Ludwig Deutsch (1855–1935); *A Palace Guard;* 1892; oil on canvas; 52⅜" x 33" (132.4 x 83.8 cm)

041. Narcisse de la Peña (1808–1876); *Oriental Woman and Her Daughter;* 1865; oil on panel; 18⅛" x 11¾" (45.4 x 29.9 cm)

042. Sir Frank Dicksee (1853–1928); *Leila;* 1892; oil on panel; 40" x 50" (101.6 x 127 cm)

043. Charles Dufresne (1876–1938); *Patio in Algiers;* 1912; oil on canvas; 29⅞" x 51⅛" (76 x 130 cm)

044. Rudolf Ernst (1854–1932); *Femmes filant au Maroc;* [n.d.]; oil on panel; 31½" x 39⅜" (80 x 100 cm)

045. Rudolf Ernst (1854–1932); *The Hookah Smoker;* [n.d.]; oil on panel. 18⅛" x 14½" (46 x 37 cm)

046. James Fairman (1826–1904); *Sunset;* [n.d.]; oil on canvas; 31⅞" x 44½" (81 x 113 cm)

047. Antoine de Favray (1706–1798); *Turkish Women;* c. 1754; oil on canvas; 36⅝" x 48⅞" (93 x 124 cm)

048. Henry Ferguson (1842–1911); *Mosque of Sultan Hassan, Cairo;* [n.d.]; oil on canvas; 25½" x 18½" (64.7 x 46.9 cm)

049. Ludwig Hans Fischer (1848–1915); *The Simoom;* [n.d.]; oil on canvas; 69¼" x 46" (175.3 x 118 cm)

050. Auguste de Forbin (1779–1841); *View of Jerusalem near the Valley of Jehoshaphat;* 1825; oil on canvas; 35⅞" x 50⅜" (91 x 128 cm)

051. Mariano Fortuny (1835–1874); *The Café of the Swallows;* 1868; watercolor; 19½" x 15½" (49.5 x 39.5 cm)

052. Eugène Fromentin (1820–1876); *The Heron Hunt (Algeria);* 1865; oil on canvas; 39" x 55⅞" (99 x 142 cm)

053. Eugène Fromentin (1820–1876); *Arab Falconer;* 1863; oil on canvas; 42½" x 28¾" (108 x 73 cm)

054. Eugène Fromentin (1820–1876); *A Street in El-Aghouat;* 1859; oil on canvas; 55⅞" x 40½" (142 x 103 cm)

055. Jean-Léon Gérôme (1824–1904); *The Carpet Merchant;* c. 1887; oil on canvas; 32⅞" x 25½" (83.5 x 64.8 cm)

056. Jean-Léon Gérôme (1824–1904); *Le Muezzin, the Call to Prayer;* 1865; oil on canvas; 31½" x 25⅛" (81 x 61.5 cm)

057. Jean-Léon Gérôme (1824–1904); *The Whirling Dervishes;* 1899; oil on canvas; 28½" x 37" (72.5 x 94 cm)

058. Jean-Léon Gérôme (1824–1904); *Interior of a Mosque;* 1870; oil on canvas; 22½" x 35" (57 x 89 cm)

059. Jean-Léon Gérôme (1824–1904); *Pool in a Harem;* 1876; oil on canvas; 28½" x 24½" (72.3 x 61.5 cm)

060. Jean-Léon Gérôme (1824–1904); *A Café in Cairo;* c. 1883; oil on canvas; 21½" x 24¾" (54.6 x 62.9 cm)

061. Nicolaos Ghyzis (1842–1901); *The Slave Market;* 1873–1875; oil on canvas; 28⅞" x 20⅞" (73.5 x 53 cm)

062. Charles Gleyre (1806–1874); *Woman of the Orient;* 1840; oil on canvas; 16⅛" x 13" (41 x 33 cm)

063. Frederick Goodall (1822–1904); *A New Attraction in the Harem;* [n.d.]; oil on canvas; 48" x 84" (122 x 213.5 cm)

064. Walter Gould (1829–1893); *An Eastern Story Teller;* 1871; oil on canvas; 43" x 54¾" (109 x 139 cm)

065. Walter Gould (1829–1893); *The Public Scribe;* 1869; oil on canvas; 43⅛" x 54¾" (109.2 x 139.1 cm)

066. Antoine-Jean Gros (1771–1835); *Portrait of Doctor Clot-Bey;* 1833; oil on canvas; 49¼" x 38¼" (125 x 97 cm)

067. Pierre Narcisse Guérin (1774–1833); *Bonaparte Pardoning the Insurgents in Cairo (23 October 1798);* 1808; oil on canvas; 143¾" x 196⅞" (365 x 500 cm)

068. Gustave Guillamet (1840–1887); *Ain Kerma (Spring of the Fig Trees), Smalah of Tiaret in Algeria;* 1867; oil on canvas; 55⅞" x 41" (142 x 104 cm)

069. Carl Haag (1820–1915); *Portrait of Jane Digby el Mezrab (Palmyra);* 1859; medium and dimensions unavailable

070. Osman Hamdy-Bey (1842–1910); *Old Man in Front of a Child's Tomb;* 1903; oil on canvas; 78" x 58¾" (202 x 150.7 cm)

071. Thomas Hicks (1823–1890); *Bayard Taylor with a View of Damascus;* 1855; oil on canvas; 24½" x 29¾" (62.2 x 75.5 cm)

072. Jean-August-Dominique Ingres (1780–1867); *Odalisque with Slave;* 1839; oil on canvas; 28⅜" x 39⅛" (72 x 100 cm)

073. Jean-August-Dominique Ingres (1780–1867); *La Grande Odalisque;* 1814; oil on canvas; 14⅛" x 25⅛" (35.8 x 63.77 cm)

074. Charles Landelle (1821–1908); *Female Fellah;* [n.d.]; oil on canvas; 51¾" x 33⅛" (131.5 x 84 cm)

075. Charles Landelle (1821–1908); *Jewish Girl in Tangiers;* [n.d.]; oil on canvas; 24⅛" x 19⅞" (61.4 x 50.5 cm)

076. Robert Scott Lauder (1803–1869); *David Roberts Esq. in the Dress He Wore in Palestine;* 1840; oil on canvas; 53⅜" x 40" (133 x 101.5 cm)

077. Jules Laurens (1825–1901); *Beginning of a Roman Road in Bithynia;* 1896; oil on canvas; 41" x 31½" (104 x 80 cm)

078. Jules Laurens (1825–1901); *Ruins of the Palace of Asraf;* [n.d.]; oil on canvas; 25½" x 21⅝" (65 x 55 cm)

079. Albert Lebourg (1849–1928); *A Street in Algiers;* 1875; oil on canvas; 17⅞" x 14⅝" (45.5 x 37 cm)

080. Jean Lecomte de Noüy (1842–1923); *The White Slave;* 1888; oil on canvas; 57½" x 46½" (146 x 118 cm)

081. Jean Lecomte de Noüy (1842–1923); *Arabs at Prayer;* [n.d.]; oil on canvas; 19⅞" x 13⅞" (50.8 x 35.6 cm)

082. Jean Lecomte de Noüy (1842–1923); *The Dream of Khosru;* 1874; oil on panel; 15½" x 25½" (39.5 x 65 cm)

083. Frederick, Lord Leighton (1830–1896); *The Light of the Hareem;* c. 1880; oil on canvas; 48" x 31⅞" (122 x 81 cm)

084. François-Gabriel Lépaulle (1804–1886); *The Pasha and his Harem;* [n.d.]; oil on canvas; 36¼" x 28¾" (92 x 73 cm)

085. Henri-Léopold Lévy (1840–1904); *Bonaparte in the Great Mosque of Cairo;* c. 1890; oil on canvas; 59" x 45⅝" (150 x 116 cm)

086. John Frederick Lewis (1805–1876); *Harem Life in Constantinople;* c. 1857; gouache and watercolor; 24⅛" x 16½" (61.2 x 41.8 cm)

087. John Frederick Lewis (1805–1876); *The Midday Meal, Cairo;* 1875; oil on canvas; 34½" x 45½" (87.6 x 115.6 cm)

088. Jean Étienne Liotard (1702–1789); *A Frankish Woman and Her Servant;* c. 1750; oil on canvas; 28½" x 22½" (72.4 x 57.2 cm)

089. Jean Étienne Liotard (1702–1789); *Portrait of M. Levett and of Mlle Glavany Seated on a Sofa;* [n.d.]; oil on card; 9¾" x 14⅜" (24.7 x 36.4 cm)

090. William Logsdail (1858–1944); *The Gates of Khalif;* 1887; oil on canvas; 44" x 32" (111 x 81 cm)

091. Vincenzo Marinelli (1820–1892); *The Dance of the Bee in the Harem;* 1862; oil on canvas; 74" x 106¼" (188 x 270 cm)

092. Peder Mønsted (1859–1941); *Portrait of a Nubian;* [n.d.]; oil on panel; 9¼" x 7½" (23.4 x 19 cm)

093. Gustave Moreau (1826–1898); *Cleopatra;* c. 1887; watercolor with gouache highlights; 15¾" x 9⅞" (40 x 25 cm)

094. Henry Siddons Mowbray (1858–1928); *The Harem;* c. 1885; oil on canvas; 12½" x 14½" (32 x 37 cm)

095. Charles Sprague Pearce (1851–1914); *The Death of the First-Born;* 1877; oil on canvas; 38½" x 51½" (97.8 x 130.8 cm)

096. Henry William Pickersgill (1782–1875); *Portrait of James Silk Buckingham and his Wife in Arab Costume of Baghdad of 1816;* 1816; oil on canvas; 60" x 48" (152.5 x 122 cm)

097. Sir Edward John Poynter (1836–1919); *Young Girl Feeding the Sacred Ibises in the Hypostyle Room at Karnak;* 1871; oil on canvas; 36½" x 27¼" (92.6 x 69.2 cm)

098. Henri Regnault (1843–1871); *Summary Judgment Under the Moorish Kings of Granada;* 1870; oil on canvas; 46¼" x 37⅜" (117.5 x 95 cm)

099. Pierre-Auguste Renoir (1841–1919); *Woman of Algiers, or, Odalisque;* 1870; oil on canvas; 27¼" x 48¼" (69.2 x 122.6 cm)

100. Pierre-Auguste Renoir (1841–1919); *Arab Festival in Algiers. The Casbah;* 1881; oil on canvas; 28⅞" x 36¼" (73.5 x 92 cm)

101. Pierre-Auguste Renoir (1841–1919); *Seated Algerian;* 1881; oil on canvas; 20" x 16⅛" (51 x 41 cm)

102. Jean-André Rixens (1846–1924); *Death of Cleopatra;* 1874; oil on canvas; 78" x 113" (200 x 290 cm)

103. David Roberts (1796–1864); *The Gate of Metwaley, Cairo;* 1843; oil on wood; 30" x 24½" (76.2 x 62.2 cm)

104. David Roberts (1796–1864); *The Gateway to the Great Temple at Baalbek;* 1841; oil on panel; 29½" x 24½" (75 x 62.2 cm)

105. Henri Rousseau (1844–1910); *Sleeping Gypsy;* 1897; oil on canvas; 51" x 78⅞" (129.5 x 200.5 cm)

106. John Singer Sargent (1856–1925); *Fumée d'ambre gris (Tangiers);* 1880; oil on canvas; 54¼" x 35⅝" (139.1 x 90.6 cm)

107. George L. Seymour (1876–1916); *A Consecration of Arms;* [n.d.]; oil on panel; 13¼" x 9" (33.6 x 22.8 cm)

108. Gustavo Simoni (1846–1926); *The Halt of the Caravan;* 1885; oil on canvas; 24" x 35¼" (61 x 81.5 cm)

109. Charles James Theriat (1860–1934); *The Vegetable Seller;* 1895; oil on canvas; 18" x 14¾" (45.7 x 37.5 cm)

110. Ange Tissier (1814–1876); *Algerian Woman and Her Slave;* 1860; oil on canvas; 51⅛" x 38⅛" (130 x 97 cm)

111. James Tissot (1836–1902); *Journey of the Magi;* c. 1894; oil on canvas; 26¾" x 38½" (68.6 x 99.1 cm)

112. James Tissot (1836–1902); *Sojourn in Egypt;* 1886–1894; oil on canvas; 27¼" x 33⅝" (69.2 x 85.4)

113. Virgilio Tojetti (1851–1901); *The Harem Dancer;* [n.d.]; oil on canvas; 46" x 32" (117 x 81 cm)

114. Paul-Désiré Trouillebert (1829–1900); *The Harem Servant;* 1874; oil on canvas; 51⅛" x 38⅛" (130 x 97 cm)

115. Elihu Vedder (1836–1923); *The Questioner of the Sphinx;* 1863; oil on canvas; 36¼" x 42¼" (92 x 107 cm)

116. Elihu Vedder (1836–1923); *Egyptian Tomb at Moonlight;* [n.d.]; oil on canvas; 12" x 13" (30.5 x 33 cm)

117. Horace Vernet (1789–1863); *The Massacre of the Mamelukes at the Citadel of Cairo;* 1819; oil on canvas; 152" x 202⅜" (386 x 514 cm)

118. Horace Vernet (1789–1863); *Judah and Tamar;* 1840; oil on canvas; 50¾" x 30⅜" (129 x 97.5 cm)

119. Élisabeth Vigée-Lebrun (1775–1842); *Madame Grassini in the Role of Zaire;* c. 1805; oil on canvas; 50" x 37⅜" (127 x 95 cm)

120. William Clark Wontner (1857–1930); *Safie, One of the Three Ladies of Bagdad;* 1900; oil on canvas; 50" x 37⅜" (127 x 95 cm)